CODING
WITH SCRATCH
WORKBOOK

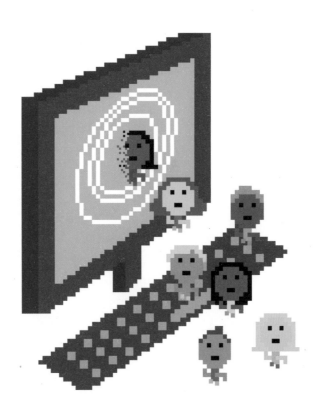

Authors and Consultants Dr. Martin Goodfellow, Daniel McCafferty,
Sean McManus, Steve Setford, Dr. Claire Quigley, Dr. Jon Woodcock
Editors Clare Lloyd, Margaret Parrish, Elizabeth Yeates
Designer Bettina Myklebust Stovne
Managing Art Editor Gemma Glover
Jacket Designer Charlotte Jennings, Jessica Lee
Producer, Pre-Production Nadine King
Producer Ed Kneafsey

First American edition, 2018
Published in the United States by DK Publishing
345 Hudson Street, New York, New York 10014

Material in this publication was previously published in
Help Your Kids with Computer Coding (2014)
Coding Games in Scratch (2015)
Coding with Scratch Workbook (2015)
Coding in Scratch: Games Workbook (2016)
Scratch Challenge Workbook (2017)

17 18 19 20 21 10 9 8 7 6 5 4 3 2 1
001—310989—Mar/2018

A catalog record for this book is available
from the Library of Congress.
ISBN: 978-1-4654-7660-9

DK books are available at special discounts when
purchased in bulk for sales promotions, premiums,
fund-raising, or educational use.
For details, contact:
DK Publishing Special Markets
345 Hudson Street, New York, New York 10014
SpecialSales@dk.com

Printed and bound in China

A WORLD OF IDEAS:
SEE ALL THERE IS TO KNOW

Discover more at **www.dk.com**

Contents

4 **Explain Scratch Code**

6 **Think Like a Computer**

8 **Becoming a Coder**

10 **What is Scratch?**

12 **Getting Scratch**

14 **Scratch Tour**

16 **Your First Project**

18 **Move It!**

20 **Which Way?**

22 **Loops**

24 **Animation**

26 **Party Time!**

28 **if-then**

30 **Variables**

32 **Math**

34 **Inputs and Events**

36 **if-then-else**

38 **A Game: Dragon!**

40 **Sound Party!**

48 **Fishball**

58 **Ghost Hunt**

64 **Rapid Reaction**

70 **Keepy-Uppy**

76 **Monkey Rescue**

82 **Memory Master**

90 **How to Build**

Tropical Tunes

104 **Better Scratch**

106 **Bad Programs**

108 **Become a Master**

Programmer

110 **Glossary**

112 **Solutions**

126 **Play the Game!**

Now get coding!

How this book works

This book introduces all the essential concepts needed to understand computer coding. Fun projects throughout put these ideas into practice. Everything is broken down into small chunks so that it's easy to follow and understand.

Boxes give handy tips and tell you what's on each page

Each topic is described in detail, with examples and exercises

Illustrations highlight different programming concepts

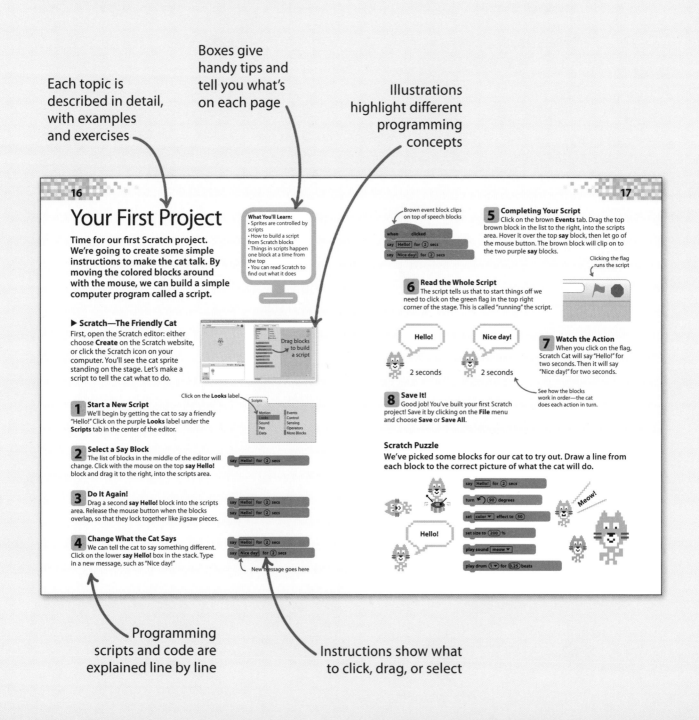

Programming scripts and code are explained line by line

Instructions show what to click, drag, or select

Labels help explain each step

Try the puzzles to show what you've learnt

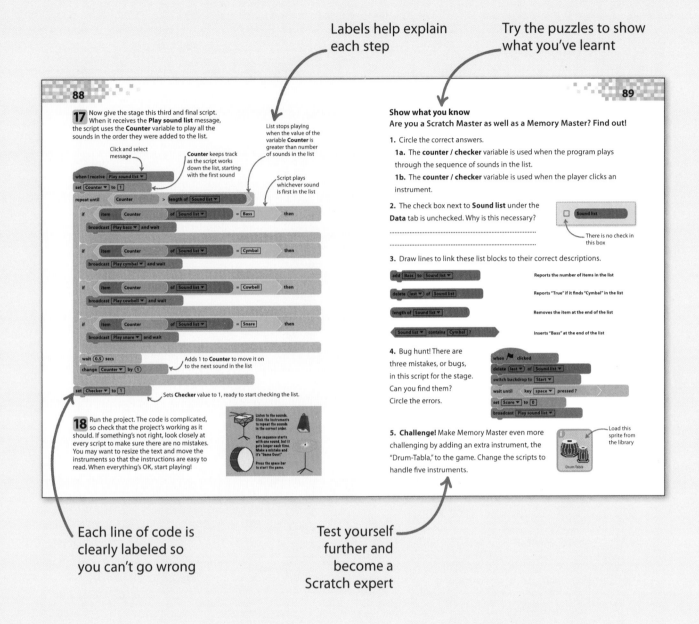

Each line of code is clearly labeled so you can't go wrong

Test yourself further and become a Scratch expert

Pixel characters help you along the way

Read on and get coding!

Think Like a Computer

A programmer must learn to think like a computer. All tasks must be broken down into small chunks so that they are easy to follow and impossible to get wrong.

Thinking like a robot

Imagine a café where the waiter is a robot. The robot has a simple computer brain, and needs to be told how to get from the café kitchen to serve food to diners seated at tables. First the process has to be broken down into simple tasks the computer can understand.

> **LINGO**
> ### Algorithm
> An algorithm is a set of simple instructions for performing a task. A program is an algorithm that has been translated into a language that computers can understand.

1 **Waiter robot program 1**
Using this program the robot grabs the food from the plate, crashes straight through the kitchen wall into the dining area, and puts the food on the floor. This algorithm wasn't detailed enough.

1. Pick up food

2. Move from kitchen to diner's table

3. Put food down

◄Disaster!
The instructions weren't clear: we forgot to tell the robot to use the door. It might seem obvious to humans but computers can't think for themselves.

2 **Waiter robot program 2**
This time we've told the robot waiter to use the kitchen door. It makes it through the door, but then hits the café cat, trips, and smashes the plate on the floor.

1. Pick up a plate with food on it

2. Move from kitchen to diner's table by:

  Move to door between kitchen and dining area

  Move from door to the table

3. Put plate down on the table in front of the diner

▲ Still not perfect
The robot doesn't know how to deal with obstacles like the cat. The program needs to give the robot even more detailed instructions so it can move around safely.

2 Waiter robot program 3

In this version of the program, the robot successfully delivers the food to the diner avoiding any obstacles. But after putting the plate down, the robot remains standing at the table while food piles up in the kitchen.

> **1. Pick up a plate with food on it holding it level at all times**

> **2. Move from kitchen to diner's table by:**

>> **Move to door between kitchen and dining area**

>>> **checking for obstacles and steering around them**

>> **Move from door to the table**

>>> **checking for obstacles and steering around them**

> **3. Put plate down on the table in front of the diner**

▲ **Success at last?**
Finally the robot can deliver the food safely. But we forgot to give it instructions to go back to the kitchen and get the next plate.

Real-world example

The waiter robot might be imaginary, but algorithms like this are in action all around us. For example, a computer-controlled elevator faces the same sort of problems. Should it go up or down? Which floor should it go to next?

> **1. Wait until doors are closed**

> **2. Wait for button to be pressed**

>> **If button pressed is higher than current floor:**

>>> **Move lift upwards**

>> **If button pressed is lower than current floor:**

>>> **Move lift downwards**

> **3. Wait until current floor equals button pressed**

> **4. Open doors**

◀ **Elevator program**
For the elevator to work correctly and safely, every step has to be precise, clear, and cover every possibility. The programmers have to make sure that they create a suitable algorithm.

Becoming a Coder

Coders are the people who write the programs behind everything we see and do on a computer. You can create your own programs by learning a programming language.

Programming languages

There are a huge range of programming languages to choose from. Each one can be used for different tasks. Here are some of the most popular languages and what they are often used for:

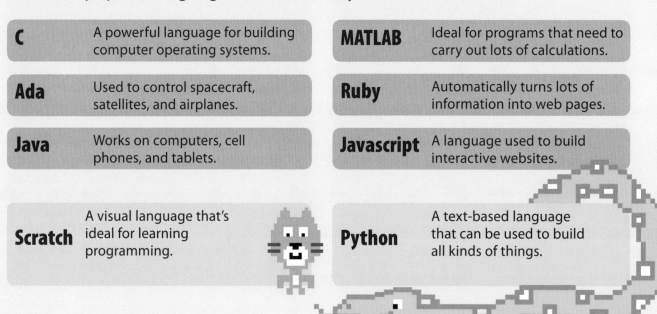

C	A powerful language for building computer operating systems.
Ada	Used to control spacecraft, satellites, and airplanes.
Java	Works on computers, cell phones, and tablets.
MATLAB	Ideal for programs that need to carry out lots of calculations.
Ruby	Automatically turns lots of information into web pages.
Javascript	A language used to build interactive websites.
Scratch	A visual language that's ideal for learning programming.
Python	A text-based language that can be used to build all kinds of things.

What is Scratch?

Scratch is a great way to start coding. Programs are created by connecting together blocks of code, instead of typing it out. Scratch is quick and easy to use, and also teaches you the key ideas you need to use other programming languages.

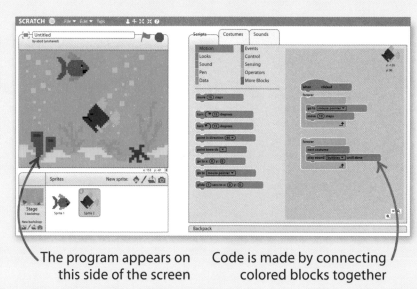

The program appears on this side of the screen

Code is made by connecting colored blocks together

What is Python?

People around the world use Python to build games, tools, and websites. It's a great language to master because it can help you build all kinds of different programs. Python looks like a mixture of recognizable words and characters, so it can be easily read and understood by humans.

```
IDLE     File     Edit     Shell     Debug     Window     Help
ghostgame
# Ghost Game
from random import randint
print('Ghost Game')
feeling_brave = True
score = 0
while feeling_brave:
    ghost_door = randint(1, 3)
    print('Three doors ahead...')
```

A program written in Python

Getting started

It's time to start programming. All you need is a computer with an Internet connection. This book is all about Scratch—the perfect language to help you on your way to becoming a coding expert. Get ready to jump into the exciting world of computer coding.

Enjoy experimenting

As a programmer you should experiment with the code and programs you make. One of the best ways to learn programming is to play around and see what happens when you change different parts of the code. By tinkering and fiddling, you'll discover new ways of doing things. You'll learn much more about computer programming and have even more fun.

What is Scratch?

A computer doesn't have a smart brain like you, so everything you want it to do must be broken down into lists of simple instructions called programs. Giving instructions to the computer is known as programming, or coding.

What You'll Learn:
• To do tasks, computers need simple instructions called programs
• Scratch is a great place to start programming
• What the ingredients of a Scratch project are

What Does a Computer Understand?

Instructions for computers have to be written following special rules and using only words the computer understands. These words and rules make up a "programming language." There are lots of different programming languages. Many have funny names, such as JavaScript, C++, and Python.

A program is a list of instructions for the computer

What is Scratch?

Scratch is a computer programming language that's easy for beginners to use. In Scratch, programs are made by joining together colored blocks using the mouse. These groups of blocks (called scripts) tell characters on the screen (called sprites) what to do. Scratch is free, safe, and fun to experiment with.

The blocks fit together like jigsaw pieces

Scratch Projects

With Scratch, you can make your own interactive stories, animations, games, music, and art. Scratch has large collections (or "libraries") of cool graphics and fun sounds you can play around with. Let your imagination run wild—you'll soon pick up the coding skills you need!

We can make lots of sounds!

What Makes Up a Scratch Project?

Here's a Scratch project. Think of it like a play. The action takes place in an area called the stage. The "actors" (the sprites) are controlled by lists of instructions (the scripts). Behind is the backdrop —the "scenery," which can be changed.

Click the green flag to run (start) a program

Backdrop (background picture)

Add a script to make the shark sprite move

Sprites are used for all the objects we want to move or control

Click the red button to stop a program

This is the stage

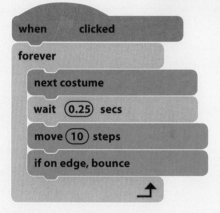

Scripts for Sprites

This is an example of a script. It makes the shark sprite bounce around the stage, opening and closing its mouth. Each block gives an instruction to the sprite. A block might tell a sprite to move, change how it looks, talk in speech bubbles, react to other sprites, or make a sound.

Show What You Know

Fill in the spaces to practice the key language of Scratch.

1. A .... is a set of instructions (program) in Scratch.

2. Objects that perform actions in a project are called ....

3. In a Scratch program, the action takes place on the ....

4. Starting a program is called .... it.

5. A collection of sounds or graphics is called a ....

Getting Scratch

You can code online at the Scratch website, but if you aren't always connected to the Internet, you can install it on your computer. Ask a grown-up to help you. **You will need the newer Scratch 2.0 for this book, not the old Scratch 1.4.**

Using Scratch Online

If you register for a Scratch account, you will be able to save your projects online and share them with friends.

1 **Sign Up for Scratch**
Go to **scratch.mit.edu** and select **Join Scratch** for instructions on how to register. You will need to get permission from an adult with an e-mail address.

2 **Create in Scratch**
When you want to use Scratch, go to the Scratch website and click on **Create**. This will open the Scratch editor window.

3 **Save in Scratch**
Projects save automatically if you're logged in to your Scratch account. You can see your saved projects by clicking on the file with an **"S"** at the top right of the screen.

Click on this file to see your saved projects

S

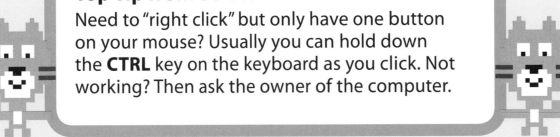

Top Tip from Scratch Cat
Need to "right click" but only have one button on your mouse? Usually you can hold down the **CTRL** key on the keyboard as you click. Not working? Then ask the owner of the computer.

Installing Scratch on a Computer

If you don't have access to the Internet or you want to work offline, you'll need the Scratch installer. Go to **scratch.mit.edu/scratch2download** and just follow the installation instructions.

To start Scratch, just double-click the **Scratch 2.0** icon on your desktop.

Scratch 2.0

Double-click the **Scratch 2.0** icon to start

Operating Systems

Check that your computer's operating system is able to run Scratch.

● The online version of Scratch 2.0 will run on Windows (PC), OS X (Macs), and some Linux computers.

● The offline version might not work with some Linux computers.

● The Raspberry Pi can't run Scratch 2.0 at the moment.

You're not in this book.

Scratch Online Community

On the Scratch website you can share your projects and try out other coders' Scratch creations. Even better, you can explore how every project works and even change ("remix") them. Look out for the buttons shown below.

Let's explore Scratch!

 See inside

Remix

Scratch Tour

Open Scratch on your computer and this is what you'll see. All you need to create and run your Scratch projects is on this screen. Take a look around.

Experiment!
• Click the buttons and tabs to experiment with Scratch. Don't worry, you won't break the computer!

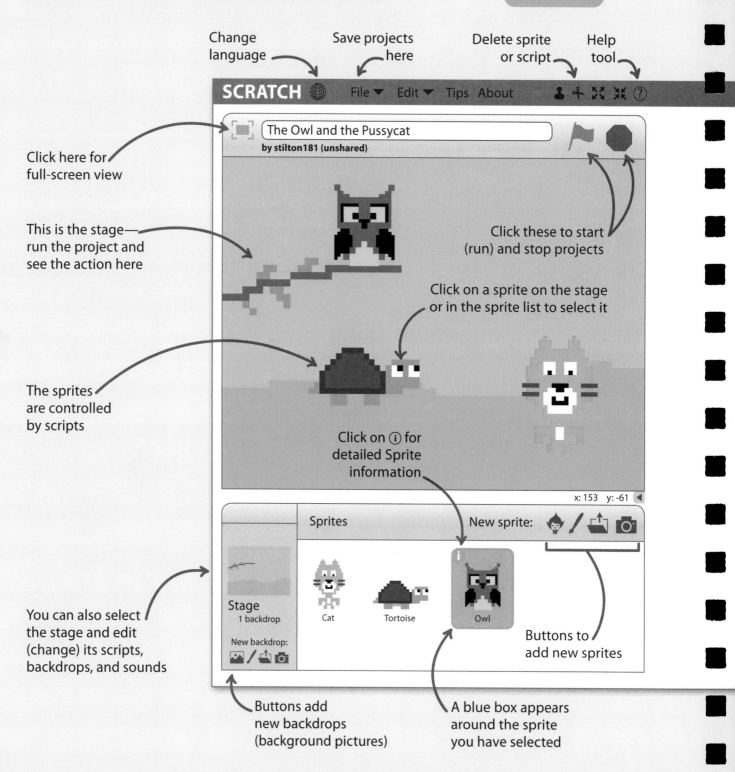

Change language

Save projects here

Delete sprite or script

Help tool

Click here for full-screen view

This is the stage—run the project and see the action here

The sprites are controlled by scripts

You can also select the stage and edit (change) its scripts, backdrops, and sounds

Click these to start (run) and stop projects

Click on a sprite on the stage or in the sprite list to select it

Click on ⓘ for detailed Sprite information

Buttons to add new sprites

Buttons add new backdrops (background pictures)

A blue box appears around the sprite you have selected

▶ Scratch Map

The stage is where projects are run. The sprite list shows all the project's sprites. Script blocks can be found in the blocks palette. Build scripts in the scripts area.

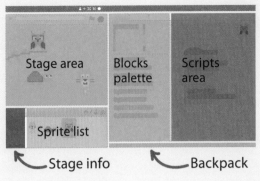

Stage area

Blocks palette

Scripts area

Sprite list

Stage info

Backpack

Costumes tab—use this to change a sprite's appearance

Scripts tab

Sounds tab—use this to change the sounds a sprite makes

Click here for step-by-step guides and tips

• Saved 🅂 stilton181 ▼

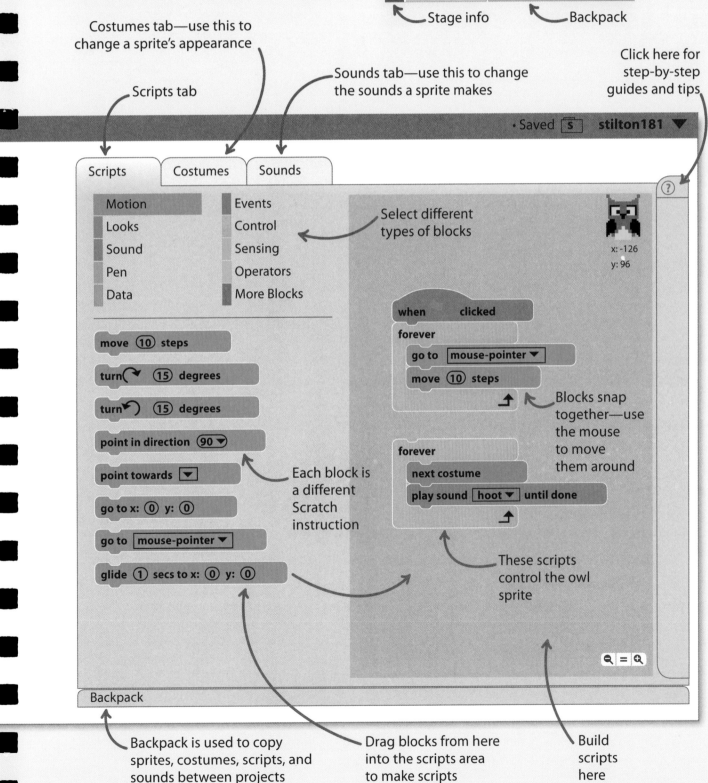

Scripts | Costumes | Sounds

Motion
Looks
Sound
Pen
Data

Events
Control
Sensing
Operators
More Blocks

Select different types of blocks

x: -126
y: 96

move 10 steps

turn ↻ 15 degrees

turn ↺ 15 degrees

point in direction 90 ▼

point towards ▼

go to x: 0 y: 0

go to mouse-pointer ▼

glide 1 secs to x: 0 y: 0

when clicked
forever
  go to mouse-pointer ▼
  move 10 steps

forever
  next costume
  play sound hoot ▼ until done

Each block is a different Scratch instruction

Blocks snap together—use the mouse to move them around

These scripts control the owl sprite

Backpack

Backpack is used to copy sprites, costumes, scripts, and sounds between projects

Drag blocks from here into the scripts area to make scripts

Build scripts here

Your First Project

Time for our first Scratch project. We're going to create some simple instructions to make the cat talk. By moving the colored blocks around with the mouse, we can build a simple computer program called a script.

What You'll Learn:
- Sprites are controlled by scripts
- How to build a script from Scratch blocks
- Things in scripts happen one block at a time from the top
- You can read Scratch to find out what it does

▶ Scratch—The Friendly Cat

First, open the Scratch editor: either choose **Create** on the Scratch website, or click the Scratch icon on your computer. You'll see the cat sprite standing on the stage. Let's make a script to tell the cat what to do.

Drag blocks to build a script

Click on the **Looks** label

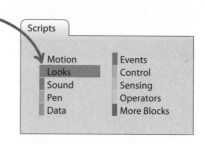

1 Start a New Script
We'll begin by getting the cat to say a friendly "Hello!" Click on the purple **Looks** label under the **Scripts** tab in the center of the editor.

2 Select a Say Block
The list of blocks in the middle of the editor will change. Click with the mouse on the top **say Hello!** block and drag it to the right, into the scripts area.

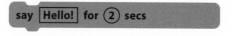

3 Do It Again!
Drag a second **say Hello!** block into the scripts area. Release the mouse button when the blocks overlap, so that they lock together like jigsaw pieces.

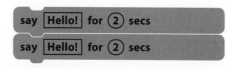

4 Change What the Cat Says
We can tell the cat to say something different. Click on the lower **say Hello!** box in the stack. Type in a new message, such as "Nice day!"

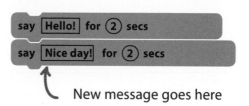

New message goes here

Brown event block clips on top of speech blocks

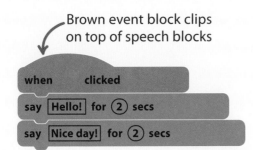

5 Completing Your Script

Click on the brown **Events** tab. Drag the top brown block in the list to the right, into the scripts area. Hover it over the top **say** block, then let go of the mouse button. The brown block will clip on to the two purple **say** blocks.

Clicking the flag runs the script

6 Read the Whole Script

The script tells us that to start things off we need to click on the green flag in the top right corner of the stage. This is called "running" the script.

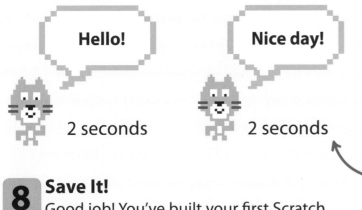

2 seconds   2 seconds

7 Watch the Action

When you click on the flag, Scratch Cat will say "Hello!" for two seconds. Then it will say "Nice day!" for two seconds.

See how the blocks work in order—the cat does each action in turn.

8 Save It!

Good job! You've built your first Scratch project! Save it by clicking on the **File** menu and choose **Save** or **Save All**.

Scratch Puzzle

We've picked some blocks for our cat to try out. Draw a line from each block to the correct picture of what the cat will do.

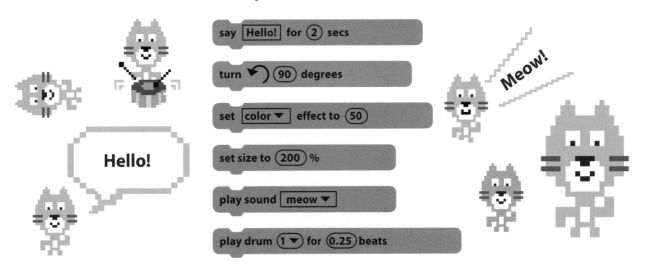

Move It!

Now for some action. Let's get our cat moving using the dark blue **Motion** blocks. Scratch measures distances in "steps." The stage is 480 steps wide and 360 steps tall. There is a block to stop sprites from getting stuck to the walls. They just bounce off them!

What You'll Learn:
• How to make a sprite move
• That Scratch measures distance in steps
• How to keep sprites the right way up

▶ Let's Move the Cat

Start a new project. Click on **File** above the stage and select **New**. Add this script and think about what the blocks do.

Click the green flag to run the script. The cat will move a short way to the right. Try it a few times.

Click on the **10** in the **move** block and type **100**. The cat now moves much further each time. Experiment by trying different numbers of steps.

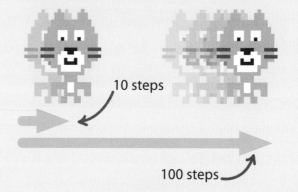

From brown **Events** blocks

From dark blue **Motion** blocks

when clicked

move (10) steps

10 steps

100 steps

▶ Bouncing Off the Walls

Now change your script to this. Read the script. What do you think it does? The **forever** block repeats the blocks inside— forever! The **if on edge, bounce** block turns the cat around at the edge of the stage.

Run the new script. The cat will now run right, then left, across the stage. Experiment —the more steps there are in each move, the faster the cat goes.

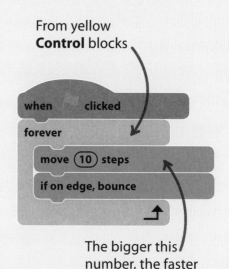

From yellow **Control** blocks

when clicked

forever

move (10) steps

if on edge, bounce

The bigger this number, the faster the movement

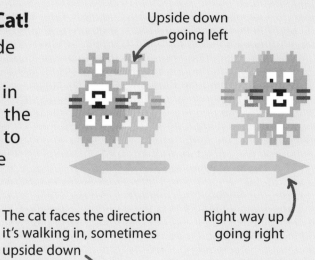

Upside down going left

Right way up going right

▶ Stop Standing on Your Head, Cat!

The poor cat spends half its time upside down—how awful! To stop this, click on the blue (i) in the corner of the cat in the sprite list. Extra information about the sprite appears. Change **rotation style** to <->. Try the other rotation styles to see what the cat does.

The cat faces the direction it's walking in, sometimes upside down

Click here to get information about the sprite

The cat faces left or right and is always the right way up

The cat doesn't rotate at all

Show What You Know
How far can you go with this quiz? All the way to the end?

1. What color are the **Motion** blocks? ....

2. Scratch measures distances in units called ....

2a. How many of these units wide is the stage? ....

2b. How many of these units tall is the stage? ....

3. A mistake in a program is known as a "bug." This script should make the cat move across the stage slowly, but when I click the green flag to run it, nothing happens! What's wrong?

....

....

....

....

We love bugs!

Which Way?

When you want to move a sprite, you need to know two things: how far and which way. Every sprite has a built-in direction arrow. When a script gets to a dark blue **move** block, that's the direction in which the sprite will go.

What You'll Learn:
• How to point a sprite in different directions
• How to make a sprite move

▶ Cat Follows Mouse!

Let's spin our cat around in every possible direction. Open a new project in the Scratch editor. Build this script for the cat sprite. Read the script. What do you think it does? Click the green flag to see if you guessed correctly.

Move the cursor around the stage and watch the cat turn around so it always looks toward the pointer. The **forever** block runs the **point toward cursor** block over and over.

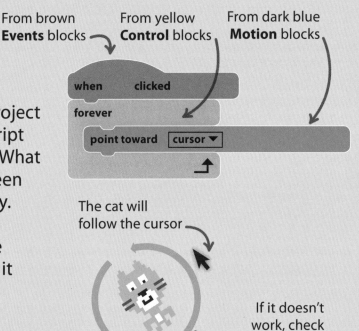

From brown **Events** blocks
From yellow **Control** blocks
From dark blue **Motion** blocks

when clicked
forever
point toward cursor ▼

The cat will follow the cursor

If it doesn't work, check rotation style

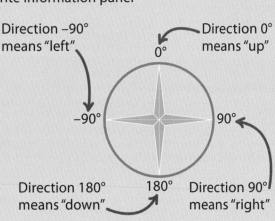

direction: –90

Direction circle shown on sprite information panel

Direction –90° means "left"

Direction 0° means "up"

0°

–90°   90°

180°

Direction 180° means "down"

Direction 90° means "right"

◀ Sprites Know Where to Go!

Every sprite knows what direction it's pointing. A sprite's direction is shown in the sprite information panel when you click the blue ⓘ.

As the cat spins around, you'll see its direction value change and the blue line pointer move around the direction circle.

Use the "compass" shown here to decode the direction number.

▶ Choosing a Sprite's Direction

We can also set a sprite's direction using the window on the **point in direction** block. You can click on the little triangle beside the number for useful directions, or just click on the window and type in a number.

point in direction (45 ▼)

Select or type in a new number to alter the direction of the cat

(90) right
(−90) left
(0) up
(180) down

Drop-down menu gives you four options

▶ Bouncing Off the Walls Again

Add the **point in direction 45** block to the "bouncing off the walls" script from page 12. Put it after the **when green flag clicked** block but before the **forever** block. Run the script. The cat will set off diagonally. Try using different directions and rotation styles.

Block goes here

when clicked
point in direction (45 ▼)
forever
　move (10) steps
　if on edge, bounce

Show What You Know
Know your way around Scratch? Then try these brain teasers!

1. What number should replace the **?** in this block to set the sprite's direction to:

point in direction (? ▼)

Up = ...

Left = ...

Down = ...

Right = ...

2. Test your Scratch script reading powers! What does this script do? Read it carefully and try to act out each block in your mind.

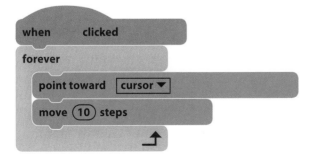

....

....

....

....

....

Loops

In computer programs, we often want to carry out the same instructions more than once. To avoid having to put down the same blocks many times, we can wrap them in a loop instruction that repeats the blocks. Meet **forever** and **repeat** loops!

What You'll Learn:
- How to repeat a group of blocks using a loop
- The difference between **forever** and **repeat** loops
- How to make some noise in Scratch

▶ Running Down the Blocks

Start a new project and make this script. Read, understand, and run it. It runs very quickly and doesn't do much.

When we run the script, each block is run in turn from top to bottom. First the cat turns a little, then the cat's color changes to green.

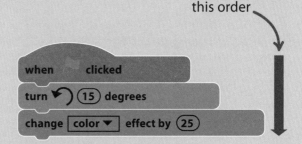

Blocks run in this order

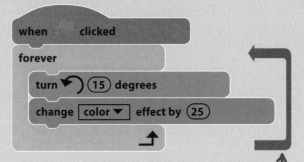

I feel a little sick!

▶ Forever Loops

A loop instruction runs a script in the normal order from top to bottom, but then loops back to the top. The loop runs the blocks inside over and over again. Try wrapping a **forever** loop around the blocks from the last script.

Now the cat turns more and changes color each time the blocks in the **forever** loop are repeated.

Press the red button to stop the loop.

When the actions finish, the program always goes back to the start of the loop

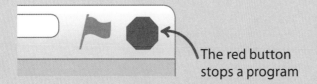

The red button stops a program

Help! I'm in a spin!

▶ Repeat Loops

If we want to repeat a group of blocks only a few times and then move on to the rest of the script, we can use the **repeat** loop block.

Try this script for a siren that annoys the cat. The **repeat** loop runs the two **play note** blocks 10 times and only then runs the **think** block. Try changing the number of repeats.

Selects buzzing

From pink
Sound
blocks

Script goes back to the start of the loop, running the blocks inside 10 times

Finished

That really is noisy!

You're not kidding!

Show What You Know
What do you know about loops? Test yourself with this quiz.

1. Loops are used to .... groups of blocks.

2. Two types of scratch loops are .... and ....

3. You can stop a **forever** loop by clicking the ....

4. In which section do you find the pink blocks? ....

5. Which block section has the loops in it? ....

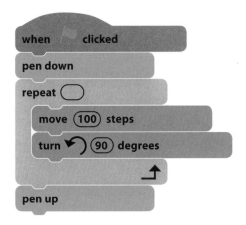

6. Bug hunt! This script should draw the four sides of a square, but nothing happens when it's run. Can you spot and suggest a fix for the bug? Programmers call this "debugging."

....

....

....

Animation

The characters in cartoons seem to move, but really you are just watching lots of slightly different pictures that fool your brain into seeing movement. This is called animation. Sprites can be animated in the same way.

What You'll Learn:
- How to animate sprites
- Sprites can change how they look
- How to use costumes
- How to load new sprites from the Scratch library

Costumes tab

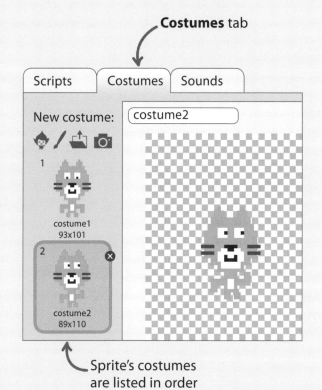

▶ Changing Costumes

Our cat sprite has two different pictures, or "costumes," it can show. Start a new scratch project and click on the **Costumes** tab just above the block list. You will then see the two costumes the cat sprite can "wear."

Sprite's costumes are listed in order

▼ Walking the Cat

To animate the cat, build and run this script. The **forever** loop repeats the **next costume** block. The picture of the sprite changes every half second, and this makes the cat look like it's walking. Try adding a **move** block in the loop to improve the animation.

This picks the next costume

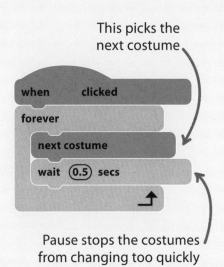

Pause stops the costumes from changing too quickly

Quickly swapping costumes makes it look as if the cat is walking

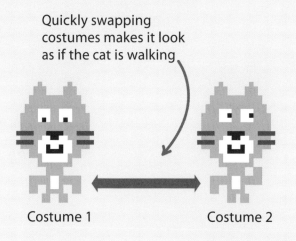

Costume 1   Costume 2

▶ Dancing Ballerina

You can use this same script to get other sprites dancing! Let's add the ballerina sprite to the project. Click on **Choose sprite from library** at the top of the sprite list. Then select the ballerina and click **OK**.

Add the costume-changing script to the ballerina's scripts area. She has four costumes. Click on the **Costumes** tab to see them. When you run the script, she uses them all as she dances on the stage.

New sprite:

Choose sprite from library

Click on the first icon to see all the sprites

Look! I'm dancing!

Let's have a party!

◀ Sprite Party!

Try adding lots of dancing sprites to your project. Choose sprites with two or more costumes. Try Dinosaur1 or some of the dancing kids.

Show What You Know
You can make sprites dance. Can you solve these problems too?

1. A different picture a sprite can show on the stage is a ....

2. .... is showing pictures with slight differences in order to make a sprite appear to move.

3. Can you rearrange the sprites below to animate a jumping pony?

Write the numbers 1 to 5 in the boxes to show the correct order.

Party Time!

We've learned a lot about making sprites do things, but a project isn't complete if it happens on a silent, white stage! Let's see how to give a project some scenery and music from the Scratch libraries to liven things up.

"party" stage

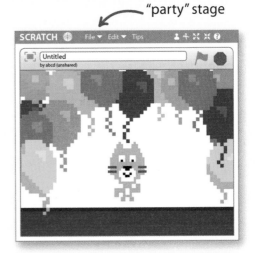

▶ Adding Scenery—Backdrops

Just as a sprite can have many costumes, the stage too can have more than one background picture, or backdrop. Click on the **Add new backdrop from library** button at the bottom left of the Stage info area.

It's Scratch Cat's birthday, so choose the "party" stage. You'll see the cat on the stage! You can load more than one backdrop. Try loading "underwater2."

You can switch backdrop in any script using the **switch backdrop** or **next backdrop** blocks from the **Looks** section.

"underwater2" stage

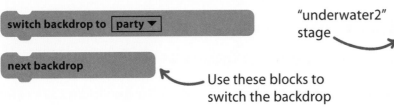

Use these blocks to switch the backdrop

▶ Light Show!

We can add scripts to the stage: click on the small picture of the stage area at the top of the Stage info area. Then try running this script with your party backdrop to bring it to life.

Continually changes the color of the stage

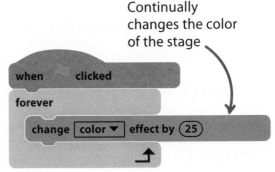

▶ Music

A party isn't a party without music! Sounds can be loaded into a sprite or the stage. But you must make scripts to play them in the Scripts area.

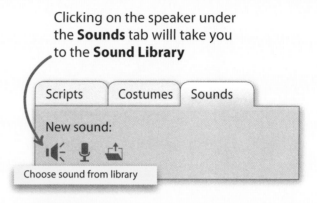

Clicking on the speaker under the **Sounds** tab willl take you to the **Sound Library**

1 **Load Some Music**
Click on the stage again. Then click on the **Sounds** tab above the blocks and select **Choose sound from library** (the speaker symbol).

2 **Select a Tune**
Choose one of the music loops, such as "dance funky," and click **OK** in the bottom right corner to load. The sound will appear on the list of sounds.

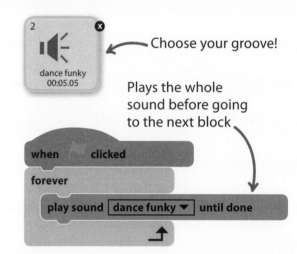

Choose your groove!

Plays the whole sound before going to the next block

3 **Make, Read, and Run a Script**
Click on the **Scripts** tab and make this script. Read the script and run it. You should have never-ending music!

Show What You Know

The cat's in the mood for a party. Are you in the mood for a quiz?

1. A background picture on the stage is called a ....

2. Circle the block that plays a whole sound before continuing:

3. True or False?

a. A project can have only one backdrop loaded. ....

b. Only the sprite that loaded a sound can play it. ....

c. The stage can have sounds and scripts. ....

d. Once you've chosen a backdrop for a script, you can't change it. ....

e. A sprite can use a script to change the stage's backdrop. ....

if-then

If it's raining, we decide to wear a raincoat. We can make this kind of decision in Scratch using the **if-then** blocks from the yellow **Control** section. Like loops, they wrap around other blocks and control when they are run.

Spin Control

Let's use **if-then** blocks to decide when our cat spins. We'll use some light blue **Sensing** blocks, which ask a "true or false?" question. Find them under the **Scripts** tab.

Sensing block goes into window at top of **if-then** block

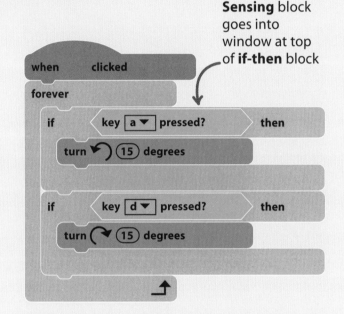

1 **Start a New Project**
Add this script. What do you think it does? The block inside each **if-then** block is only run if the answer to the question at the top of the block is "true."

Cat turns 15 degrees to the left

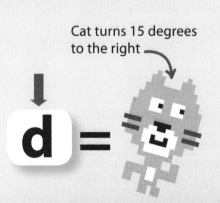

2 **Run the Script**
What happens? Nothing! Press the **"a"** key and the cat turns backward. Let the key go and it stops. The **turn** block inside the first **if-then** block is only run when the answer to the question **key a pressed?** is "true."

Cat turns 15 degrees to the right

3 **Now Press the "d" Key**
The cat turns the other way. The **turn** block inside the second **if-then** block is only run when the answer to the question **key d pressed?** is "true." If neither key is pressed, then both **turn** blocks are skipped.

A Closer Look at the if-then Block

Look at this **if-then** block taken from a script.
Read it carefully and think about what it does.

If answer's "false," blocks are skipped

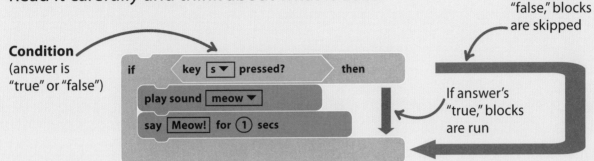

Condition
(answer is "true" or "false")

if — key s ▼ pressed? — then
play sound meow ▼
say Meow! for ① secs

If answer's "true," blocks are run

● The **if-then** block is a yellow **Control** block, because it controls when blocks inside it are run.

● An **if-then** block has a question known as a **condition**. The question must have a true/false answer.

● The blocks inside the **if-then** block are only run when the answer to the question is "true."

● If the answer to the question is "false," then the blocks inside the **if-then** block are ignored.

● Add this **if-then** to your script so the cat meows when you press the **"s"** key. Put the **if-then** block inside the loop but outside the other **if-then** blocks.

Press that key down!

S

Meow!

Show What You Know
If you're a Scratch expert, then you'll find this bug hunt easy!

This script should make the sprite change color when you press the space key, but the sprite changes color all the time. Can you spot the "bug"? ....
....
....

when clicked
forever
  if — key space ▼ pressed? — then

  change color ▼ effect by ㉕

Variables

Computers are excellent at storing information, or "data." This data could be someone's name or the weight of a cake in a competition. A variable is like a labeled box in which you can store data until your program needs it.

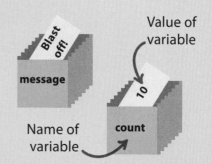

Value of variable

message

Name of variable

count

A Box with a Label

A variable can store a number or some words (programmers call words a "string"). The thing stored in a variable is called its value. You can change the value of a variable. Give variables helpful names to make the code easy to read.

Follow these instructions to create your first variable in Scratch.

Select **Data**

Click on the **Make a Variable** button

1 Start with Data
Select **Data** under the **Scripts** tab. Then click on the **Make a Variable** button. The **New Variable** window will pop up.

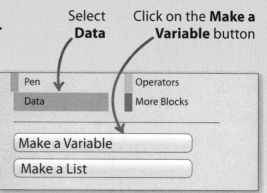

Pen | Operators
Data | More Blocks

Make a Variable
Make a List

2 Name It, Check It, Click It!
First, give your variable a useful name. Check **For all sprites**, and click **OK**. (You can ignore the **For this sprite only** box.)

New Variable

Variable name: count

● For all sprites   ○ For this sprite only

OK   Cancel

3 Get to Know Your Blocks!
Blocks for this variable will then appear in the blocks area. Make sure you know what each of the blocks does.

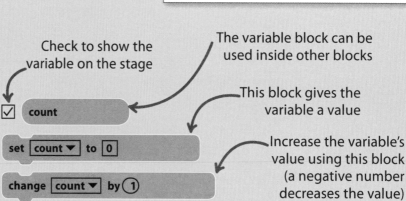

Check to show the variable on the stage

The variable block can be used inside other blocks

This block gives the variable a value

Increase the variable's value using this block (a negative number decreases the value)

☑ count

set count ▼ to 0

change count ▼ by 1

▶ Countdown Cat

Time to see some variables in action. Start a new project.

In the orange **Data** section, create two variables called **count** and **message**. Always give your variables names that explain what's stored in them.

Add this script. Make sure you drag the little orange blocks with **count** and **message** on them into the windows of the **say** blocks. Don't type the words into the **say** block windows. If you do, the cat will say the variable's name rather than what's stored in the variable.

Read the script. Can you work out what's going to happen? Now run the script.

Experiment with the numbers and text in the script. Can you make the cat count up instead of down?

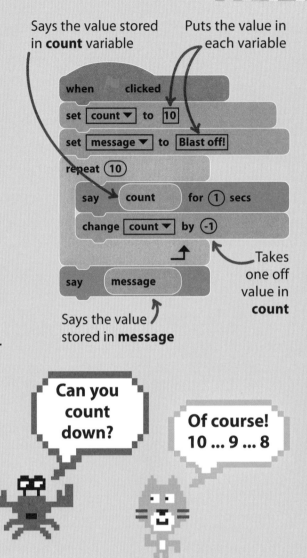

Says the value stored in **count** variable

Puts the value in each variable

Says the value stored in **message**

Takes one off value in **count**

Can you count down?

Of course! 10 ... 9 ... 8

Show What You Know
Test how much Scratch data you've stored in your brain-box.

1. A variable has a name and a ....

2. Make a Variable button is found in the orange .... blocks section.

3. Fill in the speech bubbles for these sets of blocks:

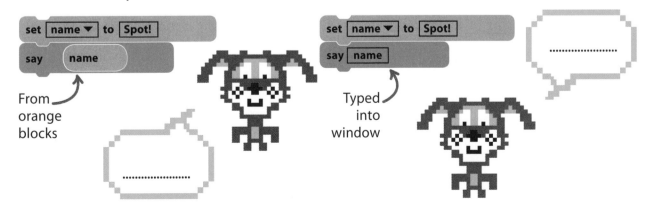

From orange blocks

Typed into window

Math

Scratch can do all the math you know about. But some of the symbols it uses are different, to fit with what's on your computer's keyboard. We can do equations in Scratch and use variables in them. Scratch can even roll dice for us.

What You'll Learn:
• How to do math in Scratch
• What math symbols computers use
• How to do equations with variables
• How to "roll dice" using the computer

▶ Math Tools

To do math you need the green **Operators** blocks. Each block does a different problem with the numbers in the two windows.

▼ Placing Operators

Wherever you put an **operator** block, it will put the answer to the problem. So if you put it into the window of a **say** block, the cat will say the answer.

Add (+)

The "+" block adds the two numbers in the block together.

Subtract (−)

The "−" block takes the second number away from the first.

Multiply (*)

Scratch uses the "*" symbol, because "x" looks like a letter.

Divide (/)

The keyboard has no division sign. Scratch uses "/" instead.

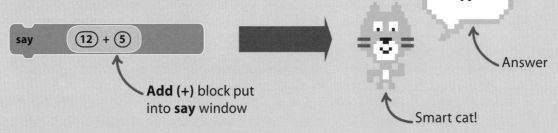

17

Add (+) block put into **say** window

Answer

Smart cat!

▶ Math and Variables

We can use **operator** blocks to solve problems with variables. For example, to find the total number of pets, we can use the **add (+)** block to add up the values of the variables **dogs** and **cats**, and store the answer in a variable called **pets**.

Add (+) block put into window of **set** block

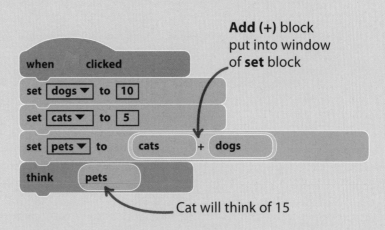

Cat will think of 15

► Throwing Dice

A random number is one that we can't predict. It's like a number we get when we roll dice—we don't know what the numbers will be before we roll. Scratch can act like dice and "roll" for us. Try this script in a new project.

Read the script, then run it. The cat will show you four random numbers as it thinks of them. Random numbers are useful in games, because they make the action difficult to guess.

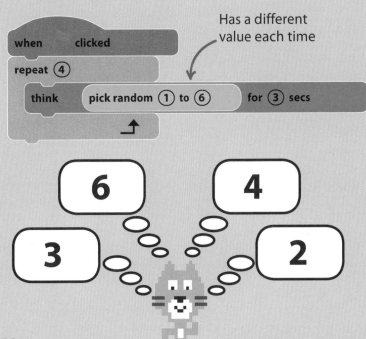

Has a different value each time

Show What You Know
Try these mathematical mind-bogglers.

1. You are the computer! Calculate the values of these blocks.

               (9) / (3)

....

2. These blocks use variables. Can you work out the answers?

              a / b

....

3. Write down the values stored in these variables.

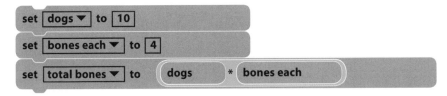

dogs: ....

bones each: ....

total bones: ....

Inputs and Events

The data put into a program, such as the answer you type when Scratch asks a question, is called input. Events are actions, like clicking a sprite or pressing a chosen key, that Scratch can use to run scripts.

The cat asks the question

What's for lunch?

You type in "Cat food"

Cat food!

Then press **enter/return** or click the blue check

What You'll Learn:
• How to ask questions and use the answers
• What an **Event** block is
• How to run a script with a key press or click

▼ Just Ask

Sprites can use questions and answers using the light blue **ask** and **answer** blocks under the **Sensing** tab. Start a new project and add this script. Read the script. What do you think it does? Run the script to test your ideas.

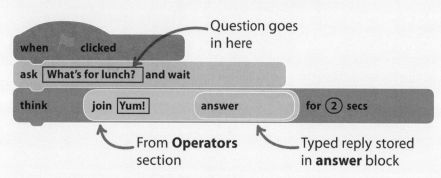

Question goes in here

when ⚑ clicked

ask What's for lunch? and wait

think join Yum! answer for ② secs

From **Operators** section

Typed reply stored in **answer** block

Lunchtime for Scratch Cat!

The cat asks the question and waits for you to type in your reply using the keyboard. When you press **enter/return**, what you typed in becomes the value of the **answer** block.

Yum! Cat food!

Answers are Like Variables

The **answer** block works just like a variable. Wherever you put the **answer** block it will be replaced by your answer to the question. The green **join** block in the script above just takes what's in its two windows and links them together as a single item.

He's always hungry!

▶ Events Trigger Scripts

Events are things that happen that the computer can tell Scratch about, such as key presses and mouse clicks. The brown **Events** "header" blocks start to run a script when a chosen event happens, in the same way that the green flag button can start a script when you click on it.

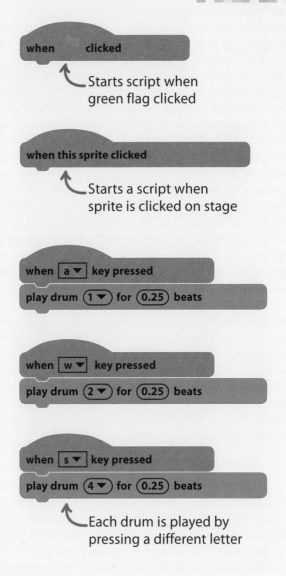

▶ Build a Drum Kit

Create lots of scripts like these. Select a different key and a different drum for each version of the script. The blocks below an **Events** header are run when you press the correct key. Play an epic drum solo using your selected keys!

Show What You Know

Can you answer these questions about inputs and Events?

1. Which blue **Sensing** block makes a sprite ask a question? ....

2. Which block holds the reply given to the question? ....

3. Something that happens to the computer, like a mouse click or a key press, is called an ....

4. What happens if I click a sprite with this script?

....

....

5. Can more than one script be running at once? ....

if-then-else

Let's meet the **if-then-else** block. This block uses a question, or **condition**, to choose between two groups of blocks to run. We'll also look at some handy **condition** blocks that use variables and values to ask "true or false?"

What You'll Learn:
- How to compare numbers, replies, and variables to make decisions
- How an **if-then-else** block works

▶ Comparing Things

There is another kind of block that asks a "true or false?" question. In the green **Operators** section there are 3 blocks that compare what's in their two windows. To read them, you need to know what these symbols mean: =, <, and >.

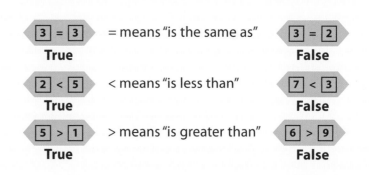

= means "is the same as"

< means "is less than"

> means "is greater than"

▶ Password Checker

An **if-then-else** block has two groups of blocks inside. It runs the first group if the condition is true, and the second group if the condition is false. We can use it to check a password.

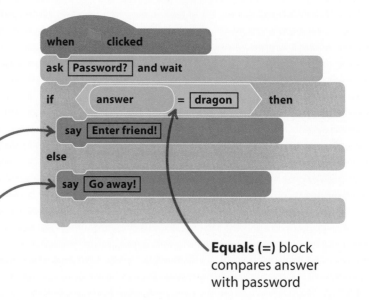

Block runs if answer is "dragon"

Block runs if answer is NOT "dragon"

Equals (=) block compares answer with password

▶ Friend or Foe?

Read and run the script. Only one of the two **say** blocks is run. The other is skipped. We get just one of the replies. If we type in the correct password, the cat greets us. Otherwise ("else"), we're sent away.

If condition is TRUE, **then**

Enter friend!

else

Go away!

▼ Free Ice Cream!

The **if-then-else** block can be used to check if you're under 10 and so get some free ice cream. One **say** block gets run, but the other doesn't. Read the script. Run it a few times with different ages.

You have to pay!

It's not fair!

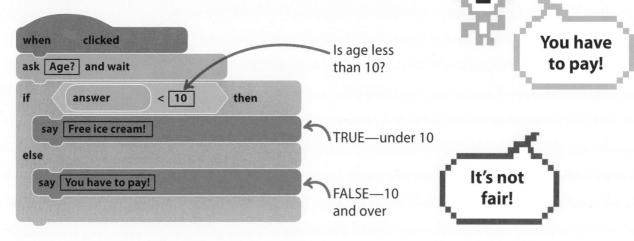

Is age less than 10?

TRUE—under 10

FALSE—10 and over

Show What You Know

Answer the questions to prove you're a smooth Scratch operator!

1. What shape blocks go into the **condition** window of an **if-then** or **if-then-else** block?

Circle the correct shape

2. Look at the variables below, then circle the green operator blocks that have the value "true."

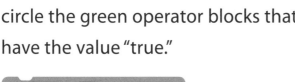

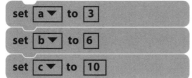 

A Game: Dragon!

We've learned a lot about Scratch so far. Now let's put it all together into a game. You are the cat. You can control where you are on the stage using the computer mouse. Avoid the ferocious dragon for as long as you can!

What You'll Learn:
- How we put a game together from sprites and scripts
- How to detect when two sprites touch
- How a script can stop a project

▶ Enter the Dragon

Add the "Dragon" sprite to the project. Add a variable for all sprites, and give it the name **speed**.

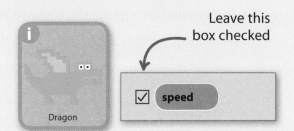

Leave this box checked

☑ speed

Dragon

▶ Get the Dragon Bouncing

Choose the dragon in the sprite list and add this script. This is the bouncing script we used before, but with a slight change. We control the dragon's speed with a variable and set the dragon off in a different direction each game. Read and run the script. The dragon bounces around the stage.

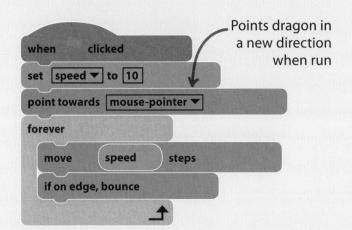

Points dragon in a new direction when run

when clicked
set speed ▼ to 10
point towards mouse-pointer ▼
forever
  move speed steps
  if on edge, bounce

▶ Mouse Controls Cat!

Now select the cat in the sprite list and add this script. Carefully read the script. It "sticks" the cat to the mouse-pointer. Inside the loop it also checks if we're touching the dragon. If we are, it stops the project—game over! Run the script to check that it works.

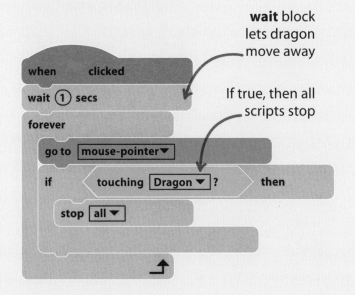

wait block lets dragon move away

If true, then all scripts stop

when clicked
wait ① secs
forever
  go to mouse-pointer ▼
  if touching Dragon ▼ ? then
    stop all ▼

▶ Score

A proper game needs a score and a challenge. Add a new variable for all sprites called **score**. Leave it checked so that it shows on the stage.

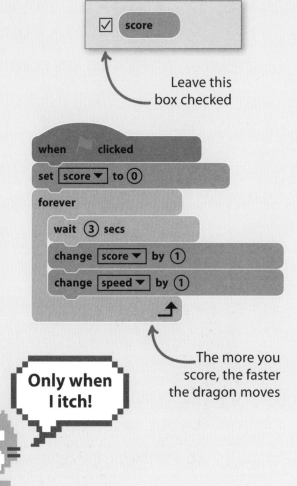

Leave this box checked

Add this script to the cat. Read it. For every 3 seconds you avoid the dragon, you score a point. But every time you score, the dragon's speed goes up one!

Run the game to see that it works as you expect. If it doesn't, check everything from the beginning. Now compete with your friends to get the best score. Why not add a backdrop and some music?

The more you score, the faster the dragon moves

Do you like Scratch?

Only when I itch!

Show What You Know

Answer the quiz—will it be a high score or "game over?"

1. Why do we leave the check box on the **score** variable checked?

....

2. How could you make the dragon go at half speed at the start?

....

3. Which block could you add inside the cat's **forever** loop to make it look like it's walking? ....

4. How many costumes does the dragon have? ....

5. What would happen if you right-clicked the dragon on the sprite list and chose **duplicate**? ....

....

Sound Party!

Computer data can be numbers, words, symbols, images, and even sounds. In this project, you'll get some party-loving sprites dancing by inputting musical sounds through your microphone!

What you'll learn:
• That you can use a microphone to make interactive projects
• How to create, control, and delete clones
• How to use Scratch's "ghosting" effect

You can place the balls and buttons anywhere you want

Sprites react to the music

Balls radiate pulses of color that spread out then fade away

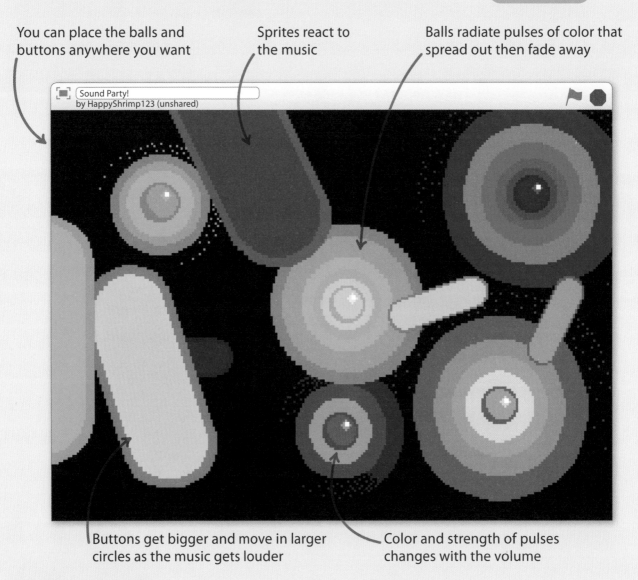

Buttons get bigger and move in larger circles as the music gets louder

Color and strength of pulses changes with the volume

▲ What you do

The action on the screen is triggered by the sounds your microphone picks up. Clicking the flag sets the oblong buttons moving in circles. Play some music to start the balls pulsing and make the buttons change size and color. The louder the music, the more on-screen mayhem there is!

Making the backdrop

The moving, pulsing shapes look much better against a dark backdrop than a plain white one. We'll start by using the paint editor to change the backdrop's color.

We love a sound party!

1 Open the Scratch editor: Either choose **Create** on the Scratch website or click the Scratch symbol on your computer. Call your project "Sound Party!" Click on the backdrop in the stage info area, then on the **Backdrops** tab.

Scripts	Backdrops

New backdrop:

1
backdrop1
480x360

Click here to select the backdrop

2 The paint editor will appear to the right of the **Backdrops** tab. Make sure that **Bitmap Mode** is selected in the bottom-right corner.

100%

Bitmap Mode
Convert to vector

Check that **Bitmap Mode** is selected

Click for block of solid color

A dark color such as black is best for this project

3 Now select the **Fill with color** tool (the paint pot symbol). Select black or another dark color on the color palette, then click on the drawing area to fill it.

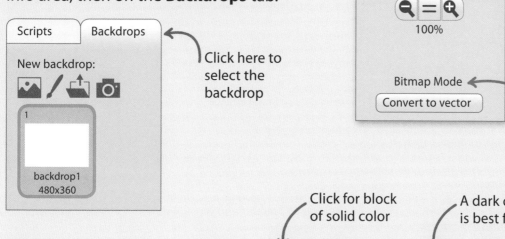

Fill with color tool

Click here for more colors

Select a color from the palette

4 We don't need the cat for this project. Right-click on the cat with the computer mouse. Choose **delete** from the pop-up menu. Goodbye, Scratch Cat!

Oh no! You'll miss the party!

Cat1

info
duplicate
delete
save to local file
hide

Creating the ball clones

The next task is to make the balls. We'll use clones to produce the pulsing effect. Clones are exact replicas of sprites. They disappear when the game or project ends.

5 Click on the sprite symbol at the top of the sprite list to go to the library. In the library, choose "Ball" and click **OK** to load the sprite into the project. The ball will appear in the sprite list.

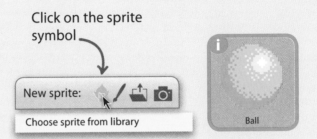

Click on the sprite symbol

New sprite:

Choose sprite from library

Ball

6 Use the colored blocks under the **Scripts** tab to build this script for the ball sprite. When music is playing, the script creates 10 clones of the ball sprite every second.

The script inside the **if-then** block runs only if the loudness of the sound input is greater than 0 (a loudness of 0 would be silence).

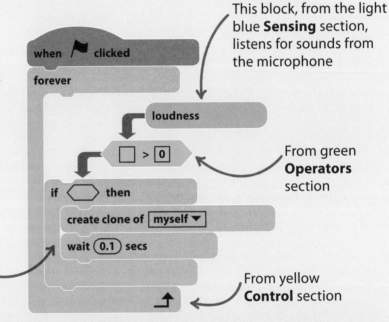

This block, from the light blue **Sensing** section, listens for sounds from the microphone

From green **Operators** section

From yellow **Control** section

when 🚩 clicked

forever

loudness

☐ > 0

if ⬡ then

create clone of myself ▼

wait 0.1 secs

Controlling clones

There are three blocks to use with clones, all found in the yellow **Control** section of the **Scripts** tab.

create clone of myself ▼

This block creates a clone of a sprite. The clone is identical to the sprite and appears in the same position and facing the same direction, so you won't be able to see it until it moves.

when I start as a clone

When a clone starts, it runs the script headed with this block.

delete this clone

This block gets rid of the clone. All clones disappear from the stage when a project stops, leaving just the original sprite.

Ghost effect

The **ghost** effect makes a sprite more transparent (see-through). It's one of seven graphic effects for changing the look of a sprite. To use them, you'll need the purple **change effect by** and **set effect to** blocks. Experiment with the effects to see what each one does.

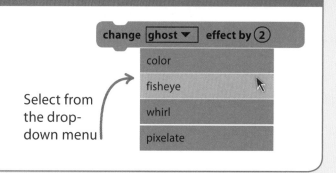

Select from the drop-down menu

7 Add this second script to the ball to control the clones. It uses blocks from the purple **Looks** section to make each clone change color, grow in size, and fade before vanishing.

repeat loop runs the blocks inside it 50 times, then stops

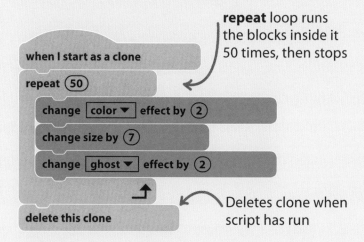

Deletes clone when script has run

8 Play some music, and click the flag to run the project. A pop-up box will appear asking you to let Scratch use your microphone. Select **Allow** (don't worry—for this project, the Scratch website will only detect sound, not record it).

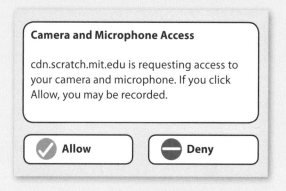

Camera and Microphone Access

cdn.scratch.mit.edu is requesting access to your camera and microphone. If you click Allow, you may be recorded.

✓ **Allow**   ⊖ **Deny**

9 Now right-click on the ball sprite and select **duplicate** from the pop-up menu. Do this four times, so that you have five balls in total. Each copy of the ball sprite will have the same code.

Select **duplicate** to copy the ball sprite and its code

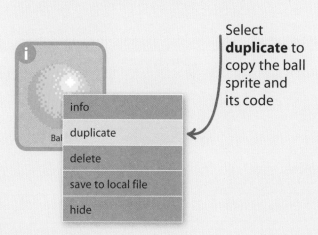

info
duplicate
delete
save to local file
hide

10 The ball has five costumes. Select a different costume for each duplicate.

Give each ball a different costume so that they are all different colors at the start

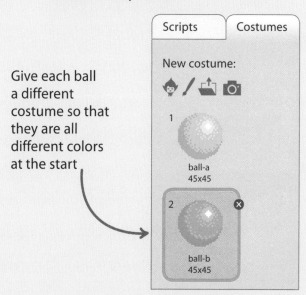

Scripts | Costumes

New costume:

1
ball-a
45x45

2
ball-b
45x45

11 Play a tune and run the project again. Try changing the values of **color**, **size**, and **ghost** in the scripts of the balls, so that each ball responds differently to the music.

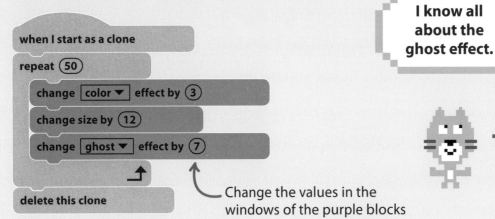

```
when I start as a clone
repeat  50
    change  color ▼  effect by  3
    change size by  12
    change  ghost ▼  effect by  7
delete this clone
```

Change the values in the windows of the purple blocks

I know all about the ghost effect.

Spooky!

Bringing in the buttons

It's time to introduce the buttons. The buttons will move in circles when the music plays. They'll also change color and size, depending on the loudness of the music.

Loudness

The **loudness** block reports the volume of sounds detected by your microphone. It gives the volume as a value from 0 to 100.

```
loudness
```

You can drop it into the window of another block to make sprites react to sound.

```
forever
    set size to   loudness   %
```

Check the block's check box to show the volume on the stage.

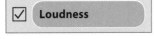
☑ **Loudness**

12 Load the sprite "Button2" from the library.

Click on the sprite symbol

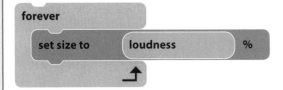
New sprite:
Choose sprite from library

Button2

13 Build this script for the button sprite, making sure that you stack the blocks in the correct windows. The script will make the button move in bigger circles as the music gets louder.

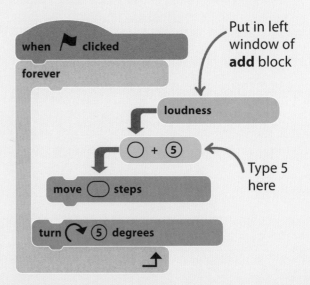

```
when  ⚑  clicked
forever
                    loudness
                    ◯ + 5
    move  ◯  steps
    turn ↻ 5 degrees
```

Put in left window of **add** block

Type 5 here

Arithmetic operators

Four blocks in the green **Operators** section allow you to do calculations. They are called **arithmetic operators**. You can type numbers into them or use variable blocks. These blocks can also be put inside one another's windows to do more difficult calculations. The inner block is solved first, then the outer block is used.

(7) + (22)
Add (+)

(64) – (28)
Subtract (−)

(11) * (10)
Multiply (×)

(120) / (4)
Divide (÷)

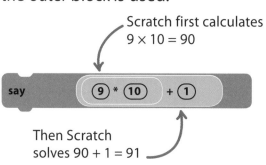

Scratch first calculates
$9 \times 10 = 90$

say (9) * (10) + (1)

Then Scratch
solves $90 + 1 = 91$

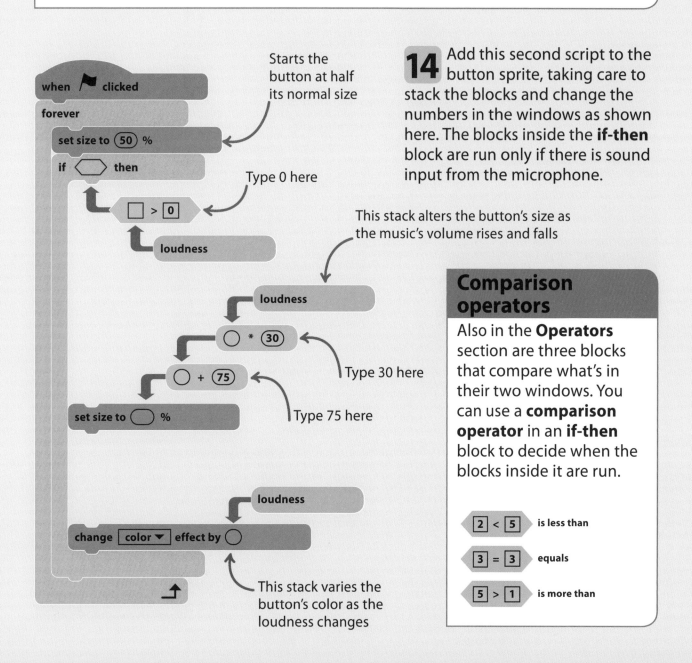

14 Add this second script to the button sprite, taking care to stack the blocks and change the numbers in the windows as shown here. The blocks inside the **if-then** block are run only if there is sound input from the microphone.

Starts the button at half its normal size

Type 0 here

This stack alters the button's size as the music's volume rises and falls

Type 30 here

Type 75 here

This stack varies the button's color as the loudness changes

Comparison operators

Also in the **Operators** section are three blocks that compare what's in their two windows. You can use a **comparison operator** in an **if-then** block to decide when the blocks inside it are run.

2 < 5 is less than

3 = 3 equals

5 > 1 is more than

15 Duplicate the button sprite five times, so that you end up with six buttons in total. Under the **Costumes** tab, select "button2-b" for three of them and keep the other three as "button2-a."

Do you like my costume?

Yes! You're one cool crab.

Try changing this value

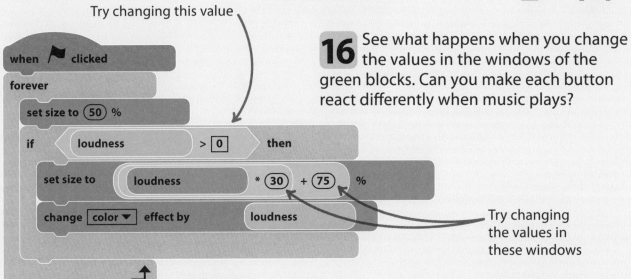

```
when clicked
forever
    set size to (50) %
    if < loudness > [0] > then
        set size to ( loudness * (30) + (75) ) %
        change [color ▼] effect by ( loudness )
```

16 See what happens when you change the values in the windows of the green blocks. Can you make each button react differently when music plays?

Try changing the values in these windows

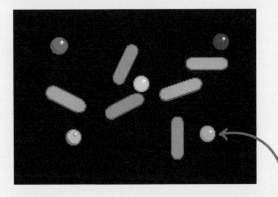

17 The balls and buttons will start from wherever they first appeared on the stage when you created them. If you think the effects would be better if they were in different places, you can move them and they will stay put and start from there!

Position the buttons and balls anywhere you like

Buttons can move over the balls, which lie behind them

18 In Scratch, the last thing you add to the stage will always appear in front of everything else. So the buttons will be in front of the balls. You can change this by altering the order in which you make the balls and buttons.

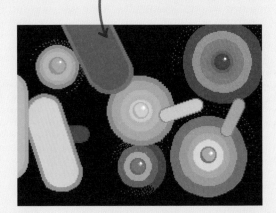

19 Congratulations—you've finished the project! Now let's get this party started!

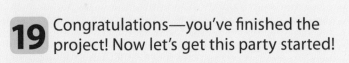

Show what you know
SOUNDS like you've got some tricky problems to deal with here!

1. The _____ block reports the volume of sounds detected by the microphone. The volume has a value between _____ and _____ .

2. This script controls the movement of the buttons. Think about how it works.

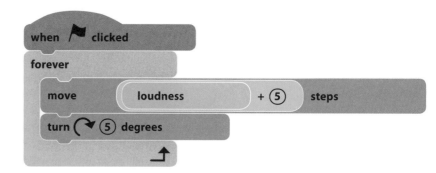

2a. How would you speed up the movement of the buttons?

....

2b. How would you make them turn in smaller circles or go the other way?

....

3. Which number should go in the empty window to make the sprite change size only if there is a very loud noise?

What should go here?

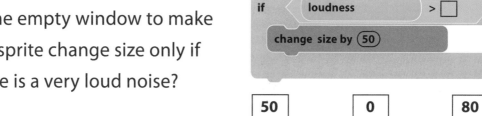

| 50 | 0 | 80 | 30 |

Circle the correct answer

4. Draw lines to link these graphic effects to their correct descriptions.

ghost ▼   brightness ▼

Makes several smaller versions of the sprite

Makes the sprite lighter or darker

whirl ▼

Twists the sprite from the middle

Turns the sprite into colored squares

mosaic ▼

pixelate ▼

Makes the sprite more see-through

5. Challenge! Instead of a black backdrop, create a backdrop that changes color to the beat of the music. You'll need to make some code for this.

Fishball

Are you ready to build Fishball? Don't worry, you won't have to do it all at once. Just follow the numbered steps and put the project together piece by piece.

What you'll learn:
• How to build simple scripts to make a game
• How to add sprites, backdrops, and sounds to improve your game
• How to keep track of the time and score

The score and time left in the game are shown here

The fish follows the ball around the stage

Use the green flag and red button to start and stop the game

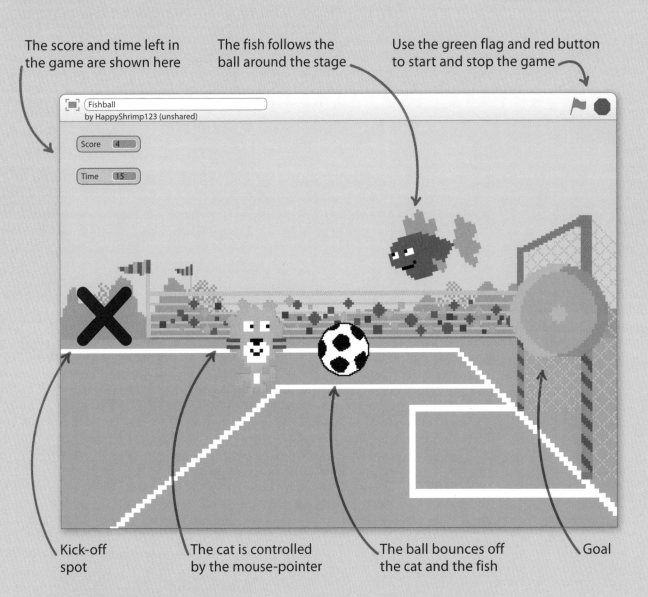

Kick-off spot

The cat is controlled by the mouse-pointer

The ball bounces off the cat and the fish

Goal

▲ Playing the game

Scratch Cat is playing soccer. Use the mouse-pointer to move him around the stage and try to deflect the ball onto the green circle to score a goal. But watch out for the fish goalkeeper—she will do her best to stop you!

Control your cat!

We'll start by creating a simple script to control the cat sprite. It will make the cat stick to the mouse-pointer like glue!

1 Open the Scratch editor: either choose **Create** on the Scratch website or click the Scratch symbol on your computer. Call the project "Fishball."

2 Under the **Scripts** tab, go to the dark blue **Motion** section of the blocks palette. Click on the **go to mouse-pointer** block and drag it to the right into the scripts area.

3 Now click the yellow **Control** section and select the **forever** block. Drag it over the **go to** block, then let go. The two blocks will lock together.

4 Next, choose the brown **Events** section of the blocks palette. Click on the **when green flag clicked** block and add it to the top of the **forever** block. Read the script through. What do you think it does?

Forever loops

Loops are sections of code that repeat again and again. A **forever** loop repeats the blocks inside it—forever! In your script to control the cat, the **forever** loop keeps the cat "glued" to the mouse-pointer for the whole game.

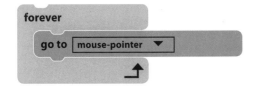

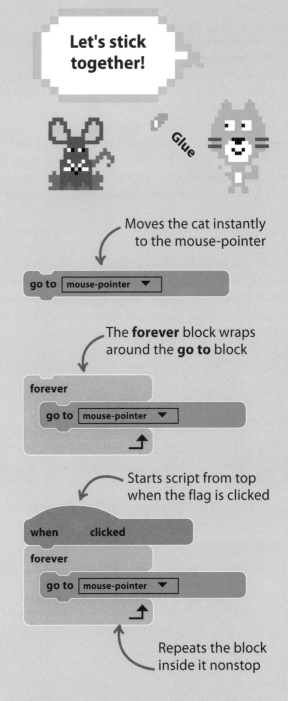

Let's stick together!

Moves the cat instantly to the mouse-pointer

`go to mouse-pointer ▼`

The **forever** block wraps around the **go to** block

Starts script from top when the flag is clicked

Repeats the block inside it nonstop

5 Click the green flag at the top of the stage to start (run) the script. The cat should move with the mouse-pointer. If not, check back through steps 1 to 4.

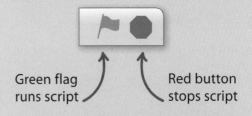

Green flag runs script

Red button stops script

Scratch Cat needs a ball

Now that you can control the cat, it's time to give him a ball to play with. You'll need to create scripts for the ball to make it bounce around the stage and off the cat.

Menus and windows

Some blocks have a "drop-down" menu, such as the **point toward** and **touching?** blocks. Click the little triangle to see the options. Then select the one you want.

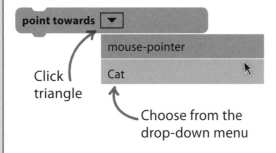

Click triangle

Choose from the drop-down menu

With other blocks, such as **turn arrow degrees**, you click in the window and type in a number.

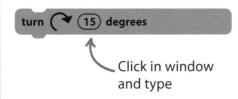

Click in window and type

if-then blocks have a pointed window into which you drag a another block that asks a question.

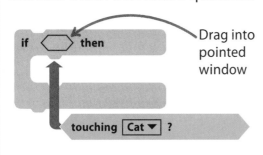

Drag into pointed window

6 Go to the sprite list and click on the **Choose sprite from library** button (the sprite symbol). In the sprite library, select "Soccer Ball" and click **OK**. The ball will appear in the sprite list.

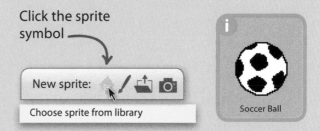

Click the sprite symbol

Soccer Ball

7 Next, put these blocks together in the soccer ball's scripts area. Remember that the color of a block tells you which section you can find it in on the blocks palette.

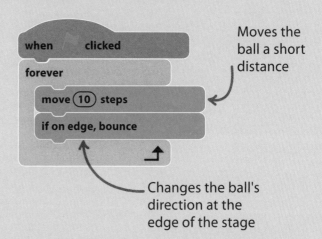

Moves the ball a short distance

Changes the ball's direction at the edge of the stage

8 Click the green flag and watch the ball bounce when it hits the edge of the stage. It won't pay any attention to the cat just yet. The green flag starts the scripts for both the ball and the cat and runs them at the same time.

I'm ignoring the cat!

9 You can make your scripts easier to understand by renaming the cat sprite. In the sprite list (below the stage), select the cat and click on the blue **(i)** in its top corner. Type "Cat" instead of "Sprite1" in the window of the sprite's information panel.

Type "Cat" in this window to change the sprite's name

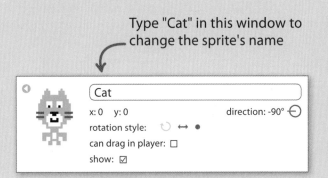

if-then

An **if-then** block wraps around other blocks and uses a "true or false?" type question to control when the blocks are run. When Scratch reaches an **if-then** block, it runs the blocks inside only if the answer to the question is true.

Is the ball touching the cat?

True   False

Bounce off Cat   Keep going

10 Now select the soccer ball sprite and put together these blocks to add to its script. Place them in the **forever** loop, after the **if on edge, bounce** block. When the ball touches the cat, the script plays a pop sound and makes the ball appear to bounce off the cat.

The **if-then** block checks to see if the ball is touching the cat

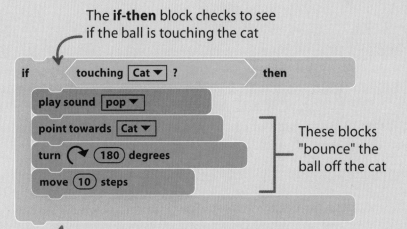

These blocks "bounce" the ball off the cat

If the ball's not touching the cat, the script ignores the instructions inside the **if-then** block

```
when    clicked
forever
    move 10 steps
    if on edge, bounce
    if        touching Cat ▼ ?        then
        play sound pop ▼
        point towards Cat ▼
        turn ↻ 180 degrees
        move 10 steps
```

11 The script for the soccer ball should now look like this. Click the green flag to test the script. The cat can now play with the ball. You should be able to move the cat around and deflect the ball by touching it. If not, check the script carefully.

Kicking off, scoring goals

Scratch Cat wants a kick-off spot and a goal to score in. A special kind of block called a variable will help you keep track of how many goals are scored during the game.

Fishball
by HappyShrimp123 (unshared)

These two sprites don't need scripts—they're just markers you can send other sprites to

Variables

A variable is like a labeled box in which you can store data, such as words or numbers. The data stored in a variable is known as its value. The new variable you made has a label, **Score**. It stores the number of goals the cat scores in a game of Fishball. The number of goals is the variable's value.

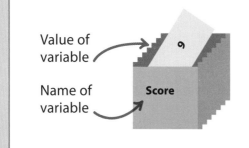

Value of variable

Name of variable

Score

12 Load two new sprites from the library: "Button1" (the green circle) and "Button5" (the black ✕). Drag Button1 to the right of the stage, halfway down, and rename it "Goal." Then drag Button5 to halfway down on the left and rename it "Start."

Sprites   New sprite:

Cat   Soccer Ball   Goal   Start

The new sprites will appear in the sprite list

13 In the orange **Data** blocks, click on **Make a Variable**. Type **"Score"** as the variable's name in the pop-up window and hit **OK**. When the block for the variable **Score** appears in the **Data** section, make sure the checkbox beside it is checked.

Type in this window

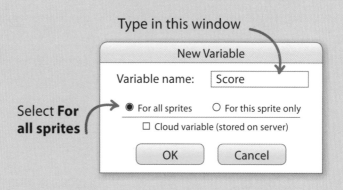

New Variable

Variable name: Score

Select **For all sprites**

● For all sprites   ○ For this sprite only
☐ Cloud variable (stored on server)

OK   Cancel

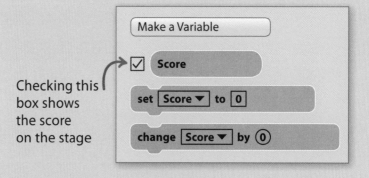

Make a Variable

☑ **Score**

set Score ▼ to 0

change Score ▼ by ⓪

Checking this box shows the score on the stage

14 Next, put these two blocks into the soccer ball's script after the **when green flag clicked** block and before the **forever** loop. The orange **set to** block sets the score to zero at the beginning of the game. The dark blue **go to** block sends the ball to the black × ready for the kick-off.

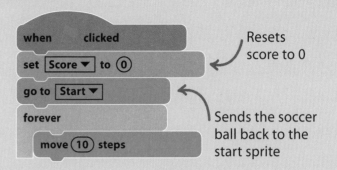

Resets score to 0

Sends the soccer ball back to the start sprite

15 You can add a sound to signal when a goal is scored. Select the soccer ball, go to the **Sounds** tab, and click on **Choose sound from library** (the speaker symbol). In the library, select "rattle" and click **OK** to load it into the project.

Sounds for the sprite can be seen under this tab

Click on the speaker symbol to go to the sound library

The "rattle" sound will appear under the **Sounds** tab

I prefer tennis!

16 Click on the **Scripts** tab and insert the group of blocks below into the ball's script. Place it under the first **if-then** group, but not inside it. Make sure it is still inside the **forever** loop. You can see the whole script in the next step.

This block, from **Sensing** section, detects when ball touches goal

Rattle sound plays each time a goal is scored

The blocks inside the **if-then** block are run only when the ball is touching the goal

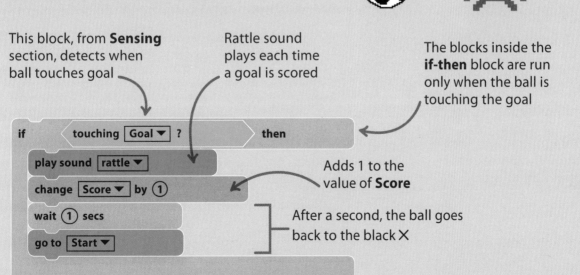

Adds 1 to the value of **Score**

After a second, the ball goes back to the black ×

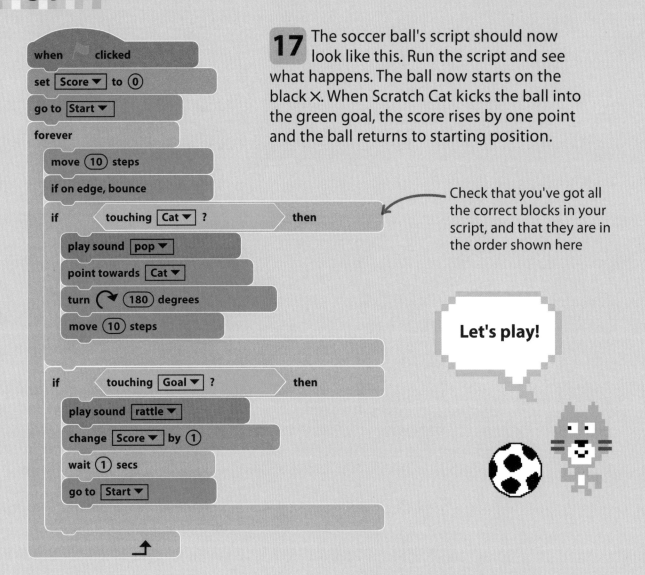

```
when [flag] clicked
set Score to 0
go to Start
forever
    move 10 steps
    if on edge, bounce
    if < touching Cat ? > then
        play sound pop
        point towards Cat
        turn ↻ 180 degrees
        move 10 steps
    if < touching Goal ? > then
        play sound rattle
        change Score by 1
        wait 1 secs
        go to Start
```

17 The soccer ball's script should now look like this. Run the script and see what happens. The ball now starts on the black ×. When Scratch Cat kicks the ball into the green goal, the score rises by one point and the ball returns to starting position.

Check that you've got all the correct blocks in your script, and that they are in the order shown here

Let's play!

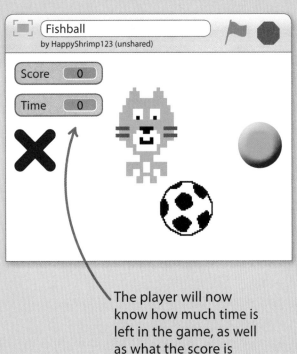

The player will now know how much time is left in the game, as well as what the score is

The pressure's on!

Games are more difficult under pressure. Adding a time limit will make Fishball more challenging. When the green flag is clicked, a 30-second countdown will start.

18 Make a new variable for all sprites called **"Time."** Leave its checkbox checked so that it shows on the stage.

Make sure this box is checked

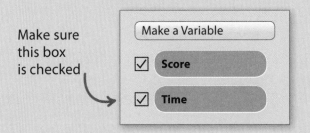

Make a Variable

☑ **Score**

☑ **Time**

19 Add this script to the cat sprite. It will run totally separately from the other script, but at the same time.

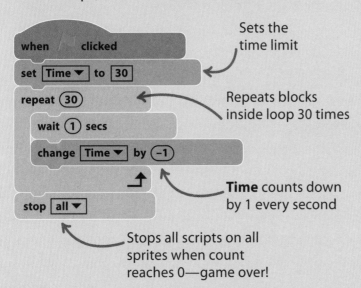

Sets the time limit

Repeats blocks inside loop 30 times

Time counts down by 1 every second

Stops all scripts on all sprites when count reaches 0—game over!

Repeat loops

A **repeat loop** repeats the blocks inside it only a fixed number of times, then the next blocks in the script are run. In your time-limit code, the loop takes 1 off the value of **Time** 30 times, then the action moves to the next block (**stop all**).

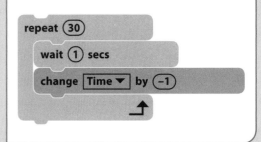

20 Try the game now. How many goals can you score in 30 seconds?

Fishy business

The game's about to get a lot harder! You're going to add a fish goalkeeper to try to stop Scratch Cat from scoring!

You'll never get past me!

21 Go to the sprite library and load "Fish1." Build the script shown on the right in the fish's scripts area. The fish should now always swim slowly toward the ball.

Fish1

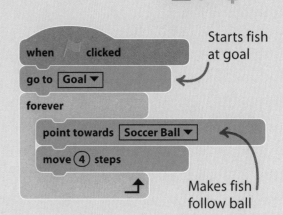

Starts fish at goal

Makes fish follow ball

22 Select the soccer ball. Add this group of blocks to the ball's script to make it bounce off the fish. (It's the same as the code that makes the ball bounce off the cat, but with "Cat" changed to "Fish1" twice.) Put it *between* the two **if-then** blocks, but not inside either of them.

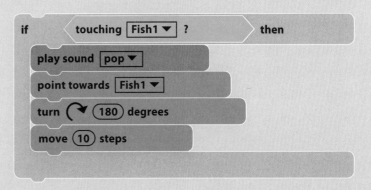

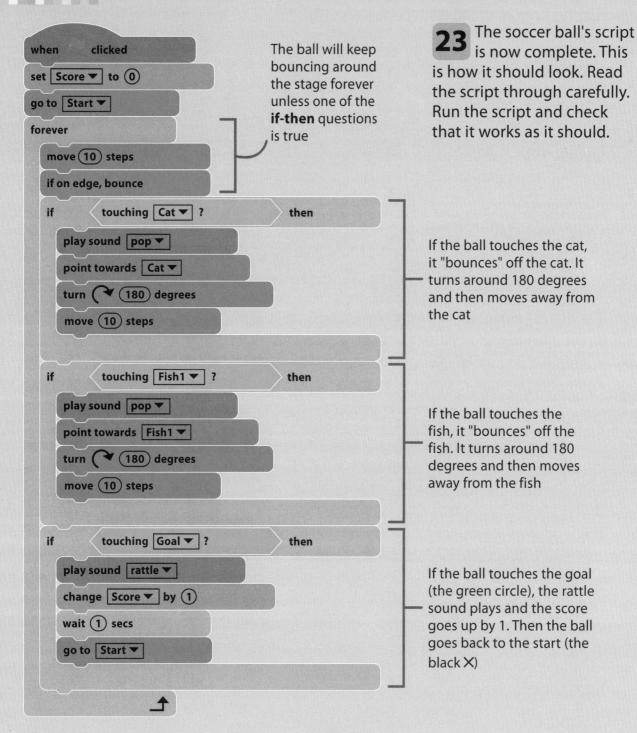

The ball will keep bouncing around the stage forever unless one of the **if-then** questions is true

23 The soccer ball's script is now complete. This is how it should look. Read the script through carefully. Run the script and check that it works as it should.

If the ball touches the cat, it "bounces" off the cat. It turns around 180 degrees and then moves away from the cat

If the ball touches the fish, it "bounces" off the fish. It turns around 180 degrees and then moves away from the fish

If the ball touches the goal (the green circle), the rattle sound plays and the score goes up by 1. Then the ball goes back to the start (the black ✕)

24 To make Fishball look like a soccer game, click the **Choose backdrop from library** button in the stage info area, at the bottom-left of the screen. Select "goal1," "goal2," or "playing field." Click **OK** to load your chosen backdrop.

Click here to go to backdrop library

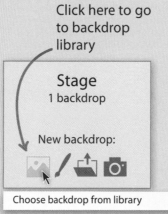

25 Good job—you've made another Scratch game! Have fun playing it! The skills you've learned while making Fishball will help you to build the other games in this book—and even to invent your own games.

Show what you know
You've aced Fishball, but can you score with this quiz?

1. Label this map of the Scratch editor, using the key below the map. Write one letter for each of the colored sections.

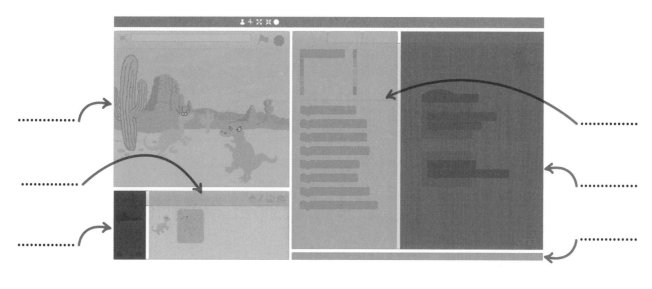

....

....

....

....

....

....

A Stage area   **B** Blocks palette   **C** Scripts area   **D** Sprite list   **E** Stage info   **F** Backpack

2. A .... repeats the blocks inside it nonstop.

3. An .... block either skips or runs the blocks inside it.

4. A .... is a block that stores data.

5. At the moment, the fish moves 4 steps at a time. Would these changes to the fish's **move** block make it swim faster or slower? Circle your answers.

Now

move (4) steps

└ Fish moves 4 steps

Change 1

move (2) steps

Faster / Slower

Change 2

move (6) steps

Faster / Slower

6. How could you make the ball move slower? ....

....

7. How could you increase the game's time limit to 40 seconds? ....

....

....

Ghost Hunt

Things get spooky in this game! You're a witch on a broomstick flying around the city at night in search of friendly ghosts. Ghost Hunt will put your keyboard skills to the test!

What you'll learn:
• How to use keyboard controls to move a sprite
• How coordinates can tell sprites where to go
• That Scratch can use random choices to make games unpredictable

The score and time left in the game are shown here

The ghost glides eerily across the screen

Use the green flag and red button to start and stop the game

You can move the witch anywhere on the screen using the arrow keys on the keyboard

▲ Playing the game

Use the arrow keys to make the witch chase the ghost. When you touch the ghost, it disappears with a pop and you score a point. But the sneaky ghost can reappear anywhere, and it floats randomly around the stage! You have 30 seconds to score as many points as you can.

Good-bye Scratch Cat, hello witch!

The player's sprite for this game will be the witch. You won't need Scratch Cat on the stage, so it's best to delete him.

1 Start a new project. Click on the **File** menu and select **New**. Call the project "Ghost Hunt." As usual, you'll see Scratch Cat on the stage.

2 Go to the sprite list. Right-click on the cat with the computer mouse. Choose **delete** from the pop-up menu.

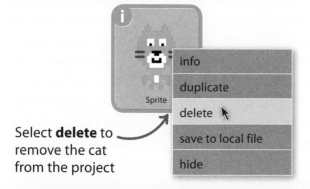

Select **delete** to remove the cat from the project

3 Click on the sprite symbol at the top of the sprite list to go to the library. Select the "Witch" sprite and click **OK** to load her into your game.

Click on the sprite symbol

New sprite:
Choose sprite from library

Witch

Coordinates

Scratch uses a pair of numbers called x–y coordinates to pinpoint a sprite's position on the stage. The x coordinate tells you where the sprite is across the stage, left or right. The y coordinate shows its up or down position. The coordinates will be positive for right and up, and negative for left and down. In Ghost Hunt, you'll use coordinates to send sprites to different parts of the stage.

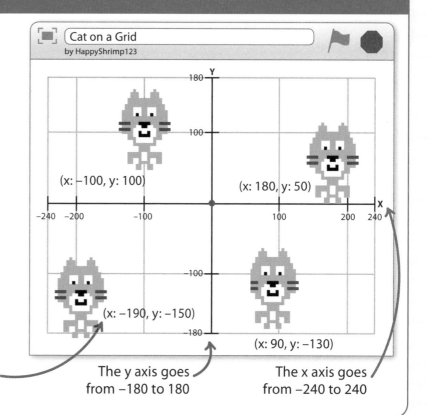

Cat on a Grid
by HappyShrimp123

(x: –100, y: 100)

(x: 180, y: 50)

(x: –190, y: –150)

(x: 90, y: –130)

The x coordinate is always written first

The y axis goes from –180 to 180

The x axis goes from –240 to 240

4 With the witch sprite selected, build this script so that you can use the arrow keys to move her around the stage.

The light blue **Sensing** blocks detect when the arrow keys are pressed

This block moves the witch 10 steps left (−10)

This block moves the witch 10 steps down (−10)

The **forever** loop makes the script check repeatedly for key presses

All the **if-then** blocks must be inside the **forever** loop

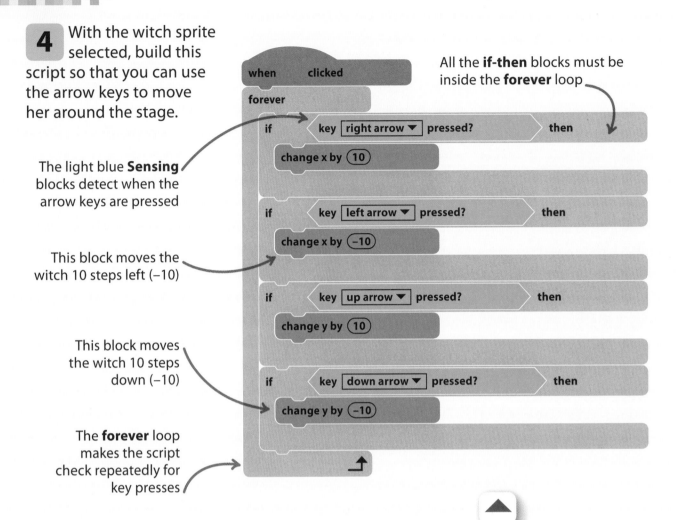

```
when [flag] clicked
forever
    if < key [right arrow ▼] pressed? > then
        change x by (10)
    if < key [left arrow ▼] pressed? > then
        change x by (−10)
    if < key [up arrow ▼] pressed? > then
        change y by (10)
    if < key [down arrow ▼] pressed? > then
        change y by (−10)
```

5 Now run the project. You should be able to move the witch all over the stage using the four arrow keys. If it doesn't work, check that you have all the correct blocks and that they are all in the right place.

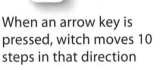

When an arrow key is pressed, witch moves 10 steps in that direction

A ghost in the city

It's nearly time to introduce the friendly ghost and get it gliding around the stage. But first, add some scenery to make the game look good.

Click here to open the backdrop library

Click OK to load it into the project

6 Go to the stage info area and click on the first symbol (**Choose backdrop from library**). Select "night city" in the library and hit **OK** to load it into the project.

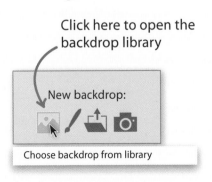

New backdrop:

Choose backdrop from library

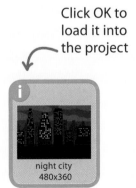

night city
480x360

7 Click on the sprite symbol at the top of the sprite list to open the sprite library. Then select "Ghost1" and click **OK** to add it to your project.

Ghost1

Random numbers

A random number is one you can't guess in advance, like rolling dice. In games, you can use random numbers to make the action difficult to predict.

8 Next, build the script shown below in Ghost1's script area. This script uses randomly chosen coordinates to make the ghost float unpredictably around the stage. Run the script.

Makes the ghost appear at the start of game

Scratch picks random coordinate numbers from within this range

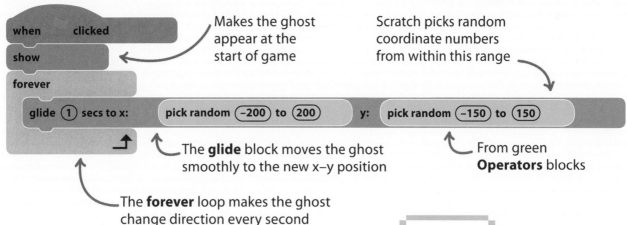

```
when [green flag] clicked
show
forever
    glide (1) secs to x: (pick random (-200) to (200)) y: (pick random (-150) to (150))
```

The **glide** block moves the ghost smoothly to the new x–y position

From green **Operators** blocks

The **forever** loop makes the ghost change direction every second

Scoring, timing, and music

At the moment, you have two sprites and a nice backdrop. To turn this project into a game, you need to set up a scoring system and a time limit. Adding some music will help to make the game more fun.

Time's running out!

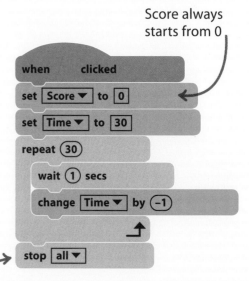

Score always starts from 0

9 Select the witch, then go to the orange **Data** section. Create two new variables for all sprites and call them **"Score"** and **"Time."** Leave their boxes ticked so they show on the stage during the game.

10 Now add this script to the witch sprite. It sets the score to zero at the start of the game. Then it counts down the seconds from 30 and ends the game at 0.

After 30 seconds, this block ends the game

```
when [green flag] clicked
set [Score ▼] to [0]
set [Time ▼] to [30]
repeat (30)
    wait (1) secs
    change [Time ▼] by (-1)
stop [all ▼]
```

Script waits here
until sprites collide

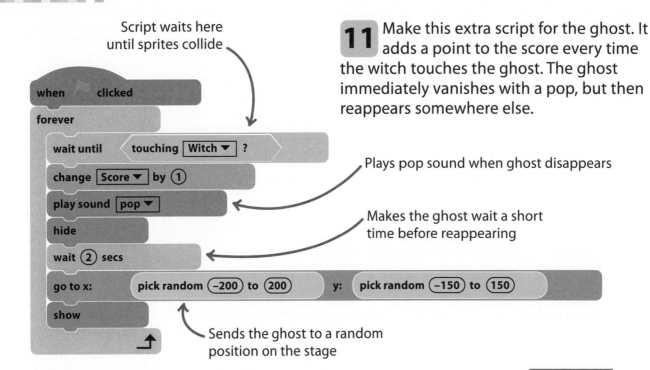

when ⚑ **clicked**

forever

wait until ⟨ touching **Witch ▼** ? ⟩

change **Score ▼** **by** (1)

play sound **pop ▼**

hide

wait (2) **secs**

go to x: (pick random (−200) to (200)) **y:** (pick random (−150) to (150))

show

Plays pop sound when ghost disappears

Makes the ghost wait a short
time before reappearing

Sends the ghost to a random
position on the stage

11 Make this extra script for the ghost. It adds a point to the score every time the witch touches the ghost. The ghost immediately vanishes with a pop, but then reappears somewhere else.

12 Run the game. You'll probably find that the sprites are so big that they bump into each other too easily, especially in the middle of the stage. To help fix this, add these two short scripts. The first is for the witch, the second is for the ghost.

Ouch!

BUMP!

Oops!
Sorry!

when ⚑ **clicked**

go to x: (0) **y:** (−140)

set size to (50) %

Starts the witch at the
bottom of the stage

Makes the witch sprite
half her normal size

when ⚑ **clicked**

set size to (50) %

Reduces the ghost's
size by half

13 For the final touch, add some music. Select the witch sprite, go to the sound library, and load "dance magic." Then add this script to loop the music.

when ⚑ **clicked**

forever

play sound **dance magic ▼** **until done**

The music plays
nonstop while
the game runs

14 Run the game again. You should find that it's more of a challenge now. Play it with your friends—who can catch the most ghosts?

It's the
witching
hour!

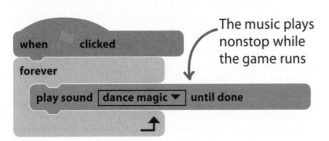

Show what you know
You're a top ghost hunter, but do these brainteasers spook you?

1. Which order are coordinates written in, (x, y) or (y, x)? ....

2. What are the coordinates of the black x's on this picture of the stage?

A. (_____, _____)   **B.** (_____, _____)   **C.** (_____, _____)   **D.** (_____, _____)

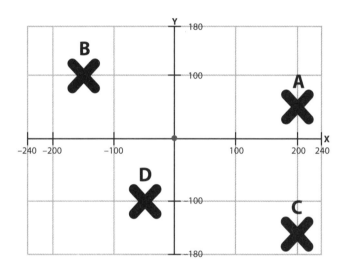

3. Add x's to the stage at these coordinates and label them a, b, c, and d:

a. (100, 0)

b. (0, 50)

c. (–100, –100)

d. (–200, –50)

4. In which direction do these blocks move a sprite: up, down, left, or right?

| change x by (100) | change y by (–150) | change y by (50) | change x by (–200) |

....

5. Circle the block that moves a sprite smoothly to a particular x–y position.

| go to x: (0) y: (0) | glide (1) secs to x: (0) y: (0) | change x by (10) |

6a. How would you make the ghost speed up? ....

....

6b. How would you slow down the witch? ....

....

7. Where would you put a **point in direction 90** block and **point in direction –90** block in the witch's main script to make her face the correct way when you press the right and left arrow keys? Try out your ideas.

Rapid Reaction

In this game, two players compete to see who has the fastest reaction time. Hit your key with lightning speed to win. If you hesitate for even a fraction of a second, you'll taste defeat!

Player 1's time is shown here

The green circle tells you which player has won

Player 2's time is shown here

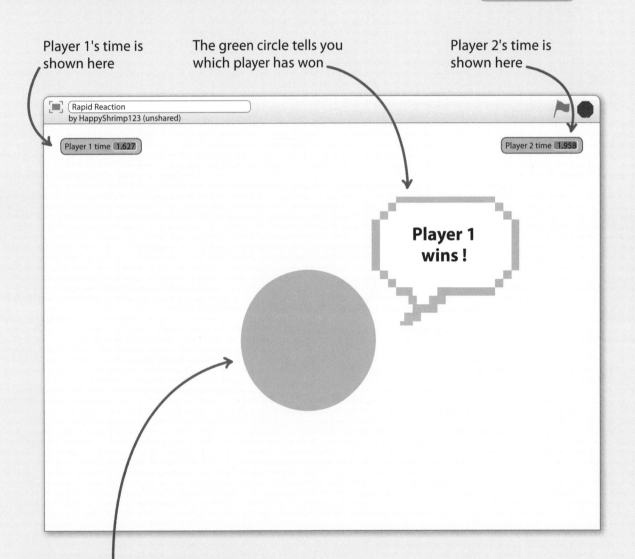

Rapid Reaction
by HappyShrimp123 (unshared)

Player 1 time (1.627)

Player 2 time (1.958)

Player 1 wins !

Rapid Reaction has only one sprite—a circle that turns from red to green

▲ Playing the game

Clicking the green flag shows the instructions on the stage. Each player has a different key to press: Player 1 the "Z" key, Player 2 the "M" key. When you're ready to play, hit the space bar. Wait until the red circle turns green, then whoever presses fastest wins the game.

Creating the big circle

There's only one sprite in this game. It's a simple colored circle that you can draw yourself using Scratch's paint editor. The circle starts off red, telling the players to wait before pressing. Then some Scratch magic turns it green to signal "Go!"

Red says "Wait!"

Green says "Go!"

1 Start a new project and name it "Rapid Reaction." Click the paintbrush symbol at the top of the sprite list to open the paint editor.

New sprite:

Click here to paint a new sprite

Circle tool

2 Check that **Bitmap Mode** is selected in the bottom-right corner of the paint editor. Then choose red on the color palette.

3 Click the circle tool on the left. Then select the solid-color shape (rather than the outline) at the bottom-left of the paint editor.

Select the solid-color shape

Choose red for the circle color

Should say **Bitmap Mode** here

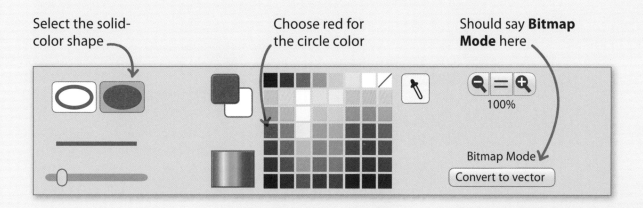

100%

Bitmap Mode

Convert to vector

4 While holding down the shift key, click and drag with the mouse to draw a circle. The circle should be a little bigger than the cat. Click outside the circle. Look at the stage to compare your circle to the cat. When you're happy with the circle's size, drag it to the center of the stage. Then right-click on the cat and select delete.

See you later!

Resizing the circle

You can use the **Shrink** and **Grow** tools at the top of the Scratch screen to make your circle smaller or bigger. Click on the tool and then on the thing you want to shrink or grow.

Shrink

Grow

Scripts for the sprites

You'll build most of the code for Rapid Reaction in the scripts area of the circle sprite. This game uses Scratch's built-in timer. You can find blocks for the timer in the light blue **Sensing** section.

5 In the **Data** section of the **Scripts** tab, make three variables for all sprites: **"Player 1 time," "Player 2 time,"** and **"Presses."** Uncheck the checkbox for **Presses.**

6 Add this script to the circle sprite. After hitting the space bar, it records how long Player 1 takes to hit the "Z" key. It also checks to see if Player 1 reacts first.

Pressing "Z" runs the rest of the script

```
when [space ▼] key pressed
wait until        key [z ▼] pressed?
set [Player 1 time ▼] to  timer
show variable [Player 1 time ▼]
change [Presses ▼] by (1)
if        < Presses      = [1] >    then
    say [Player 1 wins!]
```

Copies the time into the **Player 1 time** variable, then shows it on the stage

Adds 1 to **Presses** variable, which counts the number of key presses

If "Z" is the first key pressed, the script says Player 1 is the winner

Comparison operators

In the **Operators** section are three green blocks that compare what's in their two windows. You can use a **comparison operator** in an **if-then** block to decide when the blocks inside it are run.

```
[2] < [5]   is less than

[3] = [3]   equals

[5] > [1]   is more than
```

7 Now build the script below to record Player 2's reaction. It's almost the same as the last script, except that it's triggered by the "M" key and it uses the **Player 2 time** variable.

```
when [space ▼] key pressed
wait until        key [m ▼] pressed?
set [Player 2 time ▼] to  timer
show variable [Player 2 time ▼]
change [Presses ▼] by (1)
if        < Presses      = [1] >    then
    say [Player 2 wins!]
```

Script waits between 3 and 6 seconds after space key is pressed before changing the circle's color

8 This new script makes the red circle turn green to tell the players to press their keys. It lets the timer run until both players have pressed. If their reaction times are the same, it's a draw.

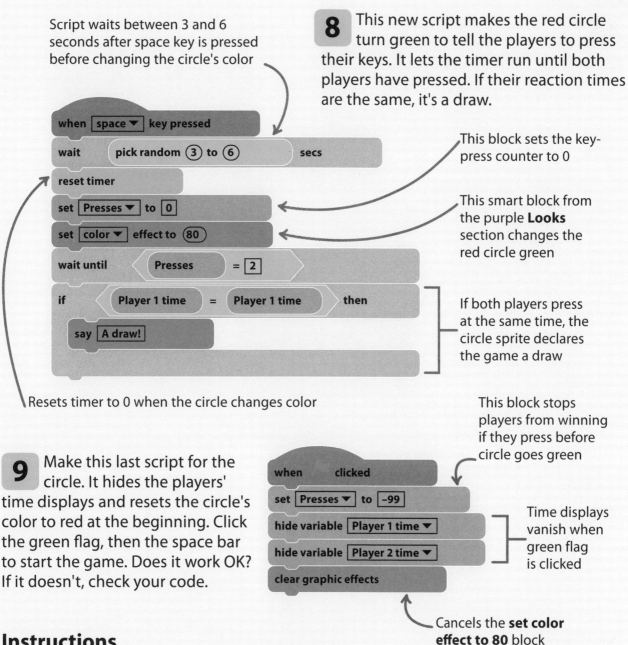

```
when  space ▼  key pressed
wait      pick random  3  to  6         secs
reset timer
set  Presses ▼  to  0
set  color ▼  effect to  80
wait until      Presses      =  2
if      Player 1 time   =   Player 1 time      then
    say  A draw!
```

This block sets the key-press counter to 0

This smart block from the purple **Looks** section changes the red circle green

If both players press at the same time, the circle sprite declares the game a draw

Resets timer to 0 when the circle changes color

This block stops players from winning if they press before circle goes green

9 Make this last script for the circle. It hides the players' time displays and resets the circle's color to red at the beginning. Click the green flag, then the space bar to start the game. Does it work OK? If it doesn't, check your code.

```
when      clicked
set  Presses ▼  to  -99
hide variable  Player 1 time ▼
hide variable  Player 2 time ▼
clear graphic effects
```

Time displays vanish when green flag is clicked

Cancels the **set color effect to 80** block

Instructions

So that the players know the rules of Rapid Reaction, you can create a special sprite that shows the instructions when the game begins.

How do I play this game?

Click on the big **"T"**

10 Your instructions sprite will just be text on a see-through background. Use the paintbrush symbol to create a new blank sprite and call it "Instructions." Make sure you are in **Bitmap Mode** in the paint editor. Then select the text tool on the left.

11 Choose black from the palette as the color for the text. Click on the checkered drawing area and type out the instructions shown on the right.

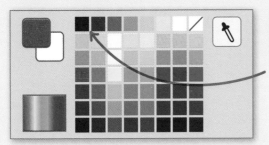

Select black for the text color

Who has the quickest reactions?

When circle goes green: Player 1 press Z Player 2 press M

Press space bar to start.

12 You can change the look of the type at this stage by clicking on **Font** at the bottom-left of the paint editor. There are six fonts to choose from. If the text doesn't fit, use the **Select** tool (the hand symbol) to resize it. Drag a box around the text and pull the corner points of the text box in or out. When you're finished, click outside the box to stop editing.

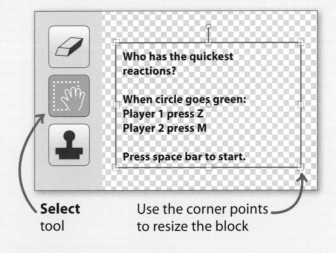

Select tool

Use the corner points to resize the block

13 Give the instructions sprite these scripts. They show the instructions at the start of the game, then hide them when the space bar is pressed. Run the game to check that the scripts work.

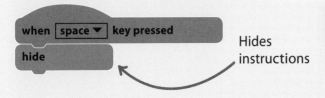

Hides instructions

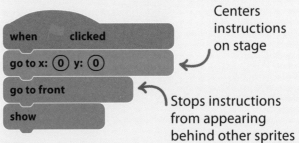

Centers instructions on stage

Stops instructions from appearing behind other sprites

14 Now go to the stage. Click on the **Player 2 time** window. Drag it into the top-right corner. This will help each player to see their time clearly.

15 Lastly, add a colored backdrop. To open the paint editor, click the paintbrush in the stage info area (bottom-left of the screen). Pick a color, select the **Fill with color** tool (the paint pot), and click on the drawing area. That's it—you're ready to play Rapid Reaction!

Fill with color tool

Paint new backdrop

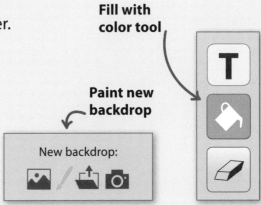

Show what you know
How will you react when you tackle these fiendish questions?

1. You can resize sprites using the .... and .... tools above the stage, at the top of the Scratch screen.

2. Which of these tools will you NOT find in the Scratch paint editor? Mark your answer.

● .... T ....

🪣 .... ✂ ....

3. In which section will you find the **timer** block? ....

4. True or false: unchecking a variable's checkbox will make it appear on the stage. ....

5. Which coordinates center a sprite on the stage? Circle your answer.

go to x: (240) y: (180)   go to x: (100) y: (-180)   go to x: (0) y: (0)

6. Try putting these numbers into the window of the **set color effect to** block. What colors do you get when the red circle changes?

20 ....   30 ....   100 ....

130 ....   150 ....   180 ....

7. What do these three comparison operator blocks mean?

a > b   c < d   d = e

a .... b   c .... d   d .... e

8. To make the game more fun, you can add sounds that play when the players press their keys. Where would you put these two blocks in the players' scripts? Try out your ideas in Scratch.

Player 1

play sound duck ▼

Player 2

play sound goose ▼

Keepy-Uppy

In this game, you use your computer's webcam to make yourself the star of the show! Test your reactions as you try to stop the falling soccer ball from hitting the bottom of the stage.

What you'll learn:
• That video can be used to input computer data
• That you can use a webcam to make interactive projects
• How to use Scratch's video blocks in scripts

Your score is shown in the corner of the screen

The ball falls from the top of the screen

You can use any part of your body to hit the ball

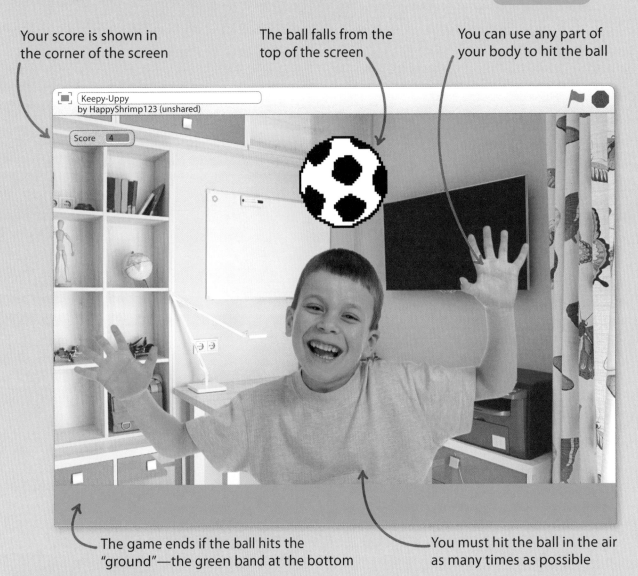

Keepy-Uppy
by HappyShrimp123 (unshared)

Score   4

The game ends if the ball hits the "ground"—the green band at the bottom

You must hit the ball in the air as many times as possible

▲ What you do

The ball reacts to movement captured by your webcam. It bounces around the stage as you use your head, hands, arms, feet, legs, or any other body part to keep it in the air. You score a point every time you touch the ball. But watch out—if the ball hits the ground, it's "Game Over!"

Begin with the backdrops

Let's start by making some backdrops. We do this first because we will need to refer to the backdrops in the scripts we build later on.

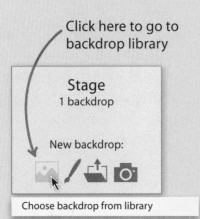

Click here to go to backdrop library

Stage
1 backdrop

New backdrop:

Choose backdrop from library

1 Start a new project and call it "Keepy-Uppy." Right-click on Scratch Cat and select **delete** from the pop-up menu. Go to the stage area and click on **Choose backdrop from library**. In the library, select "blue sky3."

2 Click in the window at the top of the paint editor and type in "Start" to rename the backdrop. Then right-click on the Start backdrop and duplicate it. Call the duplicate "Game Over!"

Scripts	Backdrops	Scripts

New backdrop:

blue sky3

Click here to rename the backdrop

1

blue sky3
480x360

duplicate
delete
save to local file

Select
duplicate

3 With the Game Over! backdrop selected, go to the color palette and choose black. Then select the **Text** (T) tool and type out the words "GAME OVER!" in the drawing area.

GAME OVER!

Text tool

Use the corner points to resize the block

Select tool

4 To change the look of the text, click on **Font** at the bottom-left of the paint editor and choose a different font. To resize the text, use the **Select** tool (the arrow symbol) and drag a box around the text. Pull the corner points of the box in or out. When you're happy with the size, click outside the box to stop editing.

GAME OVER!

I can keep this up all day!

Ball control!

You can't play Keepy-Uppy without a ball, but we can find one in the sprite library. We'll need to make some scripts for the ball so you can bounce it around the stage.

You won't get past me!

5 In the **Data** section of the **Scripts** tab, make a variable and name it "**Score.**" The check box beside it must be checked, so it can be seen on the stage.

A check in this box shows the variable on the stage

> Make a Variable
>
> ☑ Score

6 Click on the sprite symbol at the top of the sprite list to go to the library. Select the sprite "Ball-Soccer" and click **OK** to load it into your game.

Click the sprite symbol

New sprite:

Choose sprite from library

Ball-Soccer

7 We need some sounds for the ball and to announce the end of the game. Go to the **Sounds** tab and click **Choose sound from library** (the speaker symbol). Select "boing" and hit **OK**. Then do the same for "drum bass2."

Scripts	Costumes	Sounds

New sound:

Choose sound from library

Clicking on the speaker takes you to the **Sound Library**

8 Next, assemble these blocks in the ball's scripts area. The script begins the game with the sky-blue backdrop, sets the score to zero, turns on the webcam, and then sets the ball falling.

Makes ball point downward—in Scratch, down is 180, up is 0, right is 90, and left is –90

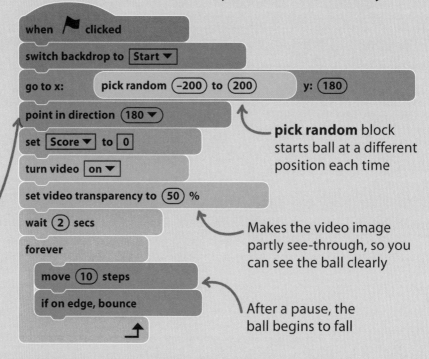

when 🏳 clicked

switch backdrop to Start ▼

go to x: pick random -200 to 200 y: 180

point in direction 180 ▼

set Score ▼ to 0

turn video on ▼

set video transparency to 50 %

wait 2 secs

forever

    move 10 steps

    if on edge, bounce

pick random block starts ball at a different position each time

Makes the video image partly see-through, so you can see the ball clearly

After a pause, the ball begins to fall

9 Now click the flag to test the script. A pop-up box will ask permission for Scratch to use your webcam. You'll need to click **Allow** for the script to run (don't worry, you won't be recorded).

10 You should be able to see yourself on the screen with the ball bouncing up and down. If you can't, check that there are no mistakes in your script.

Video blocks

As well as the **turn video on/off** block, there are two other useful video blocks.

Number range is 0–100

`set video transparency to (50) %`

High numbers make the video image more transparent (see-through). Lower numbers make it less transparent.

Click here to select **this sprite** or **Stage**

`video [direction ▼] on [this sprite ▼]`

Click here to select **direction** or **motion**

This block senses how much motion there is in the video image or what the direction of motion is, either in relation to a selected sprite or over the whole stage.

Coordinates

Scratch uses a pair of numbers called x–y coordinates to pinpoint a sprite's position on the stage. The x coordinate tells you where the sprite is across the stage, left or right. The y coordinate shows its up or down position. Coordinates get bigger the farther right or up you go, and get smaller the farther left or down you go. Keepy-Uppy uses coordinates to start the ball at the top of the stage in a random left–right position.

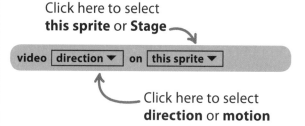

Cat on a Grid
by HappyShrimp123

(x: –100, y: 100)   (x: 180, y: 50)

(x: –190, y: –150)   (x: 90, y: –130)

The x coordinate is always written first

The y axis goes from –180 to 180

The x axis goes from –240 to 240

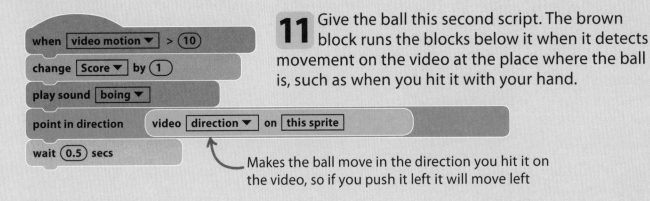

11 Give the ball this second script. The brown block runs the blocks below it when it detects movement on the video at the place where the ball is, such as when you hit it with your hand.

Makes the ball move in the direction you hit it on the video, so if you push it left it will move left

12 Now let's make another sprite. Click on **Paint new sprite** (the paintbrush) at the top of the sprite list to open the paint editor. Choose a grass-green color and use the **Rectangle** tool to draw a thick line across the bottom of the drawing area. Select the sprite in the sprite list, click on the blue **(i)** in its top corner, and rename it "Ground."

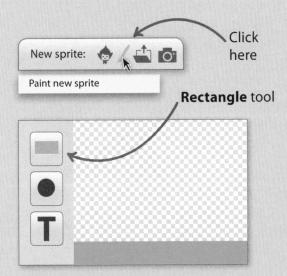

Click here

Rectangle tool

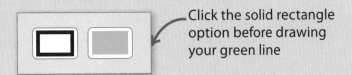

Click the solid rectangle option before drawing your green line

13 Add this final script to the ball sprite. It ends the game and turns off the webcam if the ball touches the ground (the green band at the bottom of the stage). Click the flag to test the game. If there are problems, check that the blocks in each script are in the correct order.

14 That's it—you've finished building Keepy-Uppy. Challenge your friends to see who can keep the ball in the air the longest and score the most points!

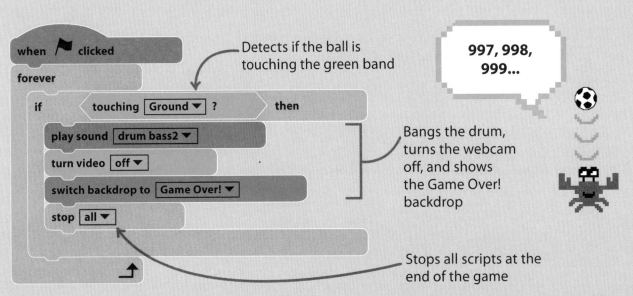

Detects if the ball is touching the green band

997, 998, 999...

Bangs the drum, turns the webcam off, and shows the Game Over! backdrop

Stops all scripts at the end of the game

Show what you know
Are your Scratch skills as good as your ball skills? Test yourself!

1. Circle the correct answers.

1a. The **turn video on** / **start camera** block switches on the webcam.

1b. We can use the webcam as **input** / **output** for a Scratch program.

1c. The **turn video off** / **stop camera** block switches off the video.

2. These blocks control the movement of the ball sprite. What happens if you change the code from **Move 10 steps** to:

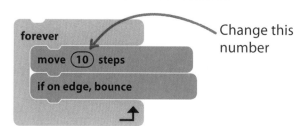

Change this number

2a. Move 30 steps ....

2b. Move 1 steps ....

2c. Move 0 steps ....

3. Read each sentence and check the correct box.

	True	False
3a. The score goes up by 2 points if you head the ball.	☐	☐
3b. When you hit the ball, a "boing" sound is played.	☐	☐
3c. The game ends if you touch the ball with your hand.	☐	☐

4. If you deleted the script you made in Step 13, would the game still work?

....

....

Change this number to 30

```
when  video motion ▼  > 10
change  Score ▼  by 1
play sound  boing ▼
point in direction    video  direction ▼  on  this sprite
wait 0.5 secs
```

5. This is the script from Step 11. If you change the **when video motion** block to **> 30**, does it make the game easier or harder?

....

6. Challenge! Add a timer and some new code so that your total score is now the number of keepy-ups + the number of seconds you lasted.

Monkey Rescue

Scrolling is sliding sprites together in the same direction so that a character appears to move through a scene. In Monkey Rescue, scrolling will make the cat fly across the city saving monkeys!

What you'll learn:
• How to make sprites scroll across the stage
• That sprites can send messages to each other
• How to make sprites appear and vanish at certain points in a game

The counters show the numbers of lives left and monkeys rescued

Starry night background

The stranded monkeys are stuck on top of tall buildings

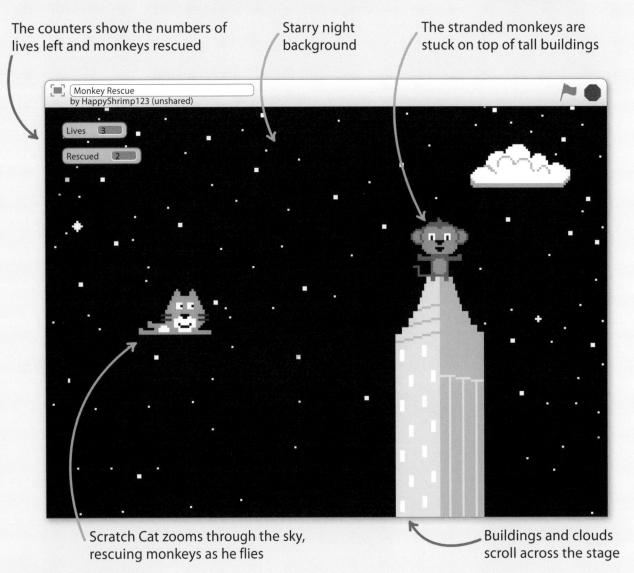

Scratch Cat zooms through the sky, rescuing monkeys as he flies

Buildings and clouds scroll across the stage

▲ What you do

Press the space bar and Scratch Cat rises in the air—do nothing and he falls downward. When Scratch Cat touches a monkey, he rescues it and it vanishes. You have five lives. Hit a building or a cloud and you lose a life. How many monkeys can you save before all your lives are gone?

Superhero Scratch Cat!

For Monkey Rescue, we'll use a flying version of Scratch Cat instead of the normal cat sprite. Let's set the scene and get him flying through the night sky over Scratch City.

I'm the big hero in this game!

1 Start a new project and call it "Monkey Rescue." Delete the normal Scratch Cat. Go to the **Sprite Library**, select "Cat1 Flying," and hit **OK** to load it.

Click the sprite symbol

New sprite:

Choose sprite from library

Cat1 Flying

2 Now add some sounds. Under the **Sounds** tab, click on **Choose sound from library** (the speaker). In the library, select "chee chee" and click **OK**. Do the same for "meow2."

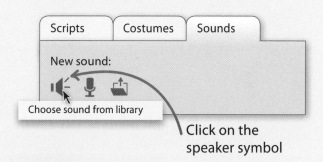

Scripts | Costumes | Sounds

New sound:

Choose sound from library

Click on the speaker symbol

3 Next, build this code in Flying Scratch's scripts area. The x–y numbers, or coordinates, tell the cat where to appear on the stage at the start. The **forever** loop causes him to drop continually. Click the flag to test the script.

Cat will appear in front of everything else on the stage

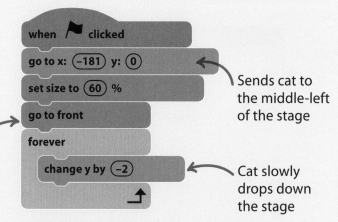

when [flag] clicked
go to x: (–181) y: (0)
set size to (60) %
go to front
forever
  change y by (–2)

Sends cat to the middle-left of the stage

Cat slowly drops down the stage

4 Give Flying Scratch this second script. It allows you to control the cat's upward movement. Every time you press the space bar, he will move up 20 steps.

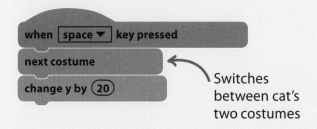

when [space] key pressed
next costume
change y by (20)

Switches between cat's two costumes

5 Go to the stage info area, at the bottom-left of the Scratch editor. Click on the **Choose backdrop from library** symbol. Select "stars" in the library and hit **OK**.

Click here for the **Backdrop Library**

New backdrop:

Choose backdrop from library

Scrolling sprites

Now that we've set the scene, let's add three more things: the buildings, the clouds that drift by overhead, and the poor, stranded monkeys.

7 Add this script to the Buildings sprite. The sprite will scroll across the stage from right to left. There are 10 costumes. The purple block picks a random costume for each pass across the stage.

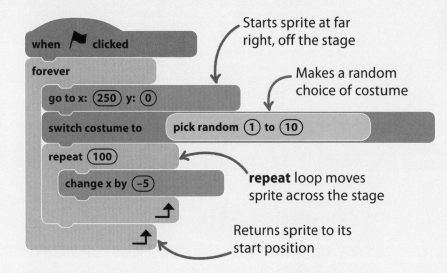

Starts sprite at far right, off the stage

Makes a random choice of costume

repeat loop moves sprite across the stage

Returns sprite to its start position

8 Now go back to the sprite list, click on the sprite symbol, and choose "Cloud." Load the sprite into the game.

Cloud

9 Put these blocks together for the cloud. It starts the cloud near the top of the stage but off to the right, then moves it across, from right to left.

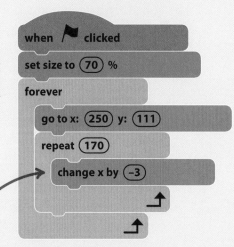

Cloud moves more slowly than the Buildings sprite

6 Click on the sprite symbol at the top of the sprite list to go to the library. Choose the sprite "Buildings" and click **OK** to load it into your game.

Click for the **Sprite Library**

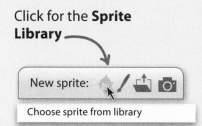

New sprite:

Choose sprite from library

Buildings

Scrolling

Although you see the cat fly through the city, he doesn't actually move forward. Instead, the buildings, clouds, and monkeys scroll (slide across the stage) in the direction opposite to the way he's facing. This creates the illusion that he's flying toward them. By randomly switching the Buildings sprite's costumes, the code makes it looks as if the cat is moving through a changing city scene.

10 Return to the sprite list and load the final sprite, "Monkey2," from the **Sprite Library**.

Monkey2

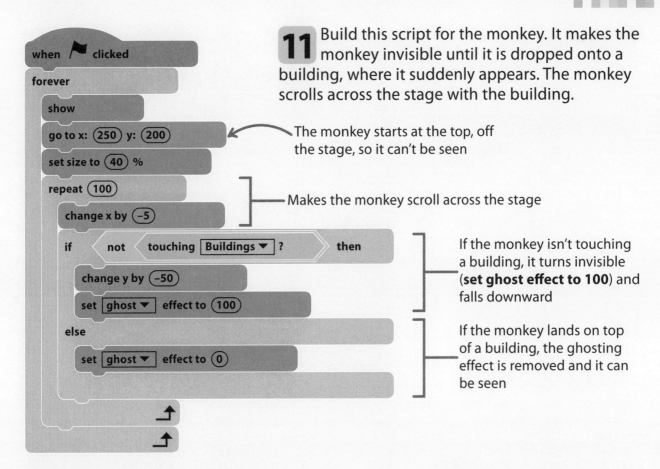

11 Build this script for the monkey. It makes the monkey invisible until it is dropped onto a building, where it suddenly appears. The monkey scrolls across the stage with the building.

The monkey starts at the top, off the stage, so it can't be seen

Makes the monkey scroll across the stage

If the monkey isn't touching a building, it turns invisible (**set ghost effect to 100**) and falls downward

If the monkey lands on top of a building, the ghosting effect is removed and it can be seen

Even superheroes need scripts!

The next task is to make some scripts for the cat to set up a scoring system and the number of lives he has before the game ends.

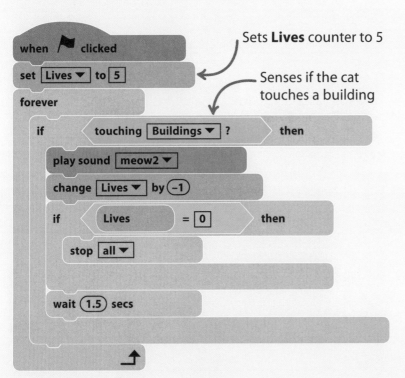

Sets **Lives** counter to 5

Senses if the cat touches a building

12 Make two variables called "**Lives**" and "**Rescued**." Make sure their check boxes are checked so they show on the stage.

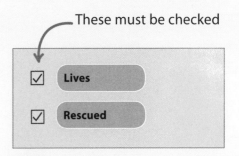

These must be checked

☑ Lives

☑ Rescued

13 Select the cat and give it this script. It sets the cat's **Lives** counter on the stage to 5. When the cat touches a building, a "meow" sound plays and a life is lost. When there are no lives left (**Lives = 0**), all scripts stop running and the game ends.

Messages

Scratch sprites can broadcast (send out) messages to "talk" to each other.

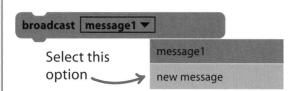

Select this option →

| message1 |
| new message |

This block sends out a message telling other sprites to do something. Click the arrow to create a new instruction.

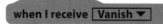

This block tells other sprites to do something, such as vanish. It waits until they finish before continuing.

when I receive Vanish ▼

This block runs any script below it when it receives a message, such as **Vanish**.

---

14 Duplicate the cat's script from Step 13, but delete the **set Lives to 5** block. Select **Cloud** in the **touching?** block. Now the cat will also lose a life if he touches a cloud.

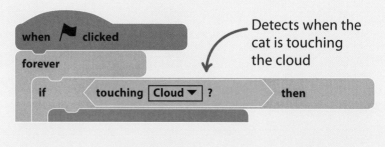

Detects when the cat is touching the cloud

15 Using a brown **broadcast** block, select **new message** from its drop-down menu. Type "**Vanish**" into the pop-up box.

Type your message in here

16 Build this new script for the cat. If the cat touches the monkey, the "chee chee" sound plays, the **Rescued** score goes up by 1, and the monkey is sent the message **Vanish**.

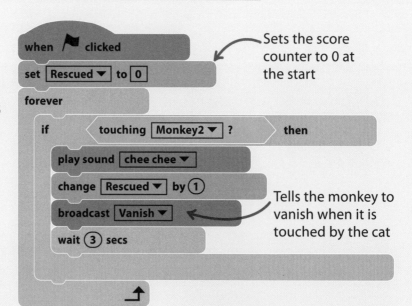

Sets the score counter to 0 at the start

Tells the monkey to vanish when it is touched by the cat

17 Create this final script for the monkey. When the monkey gets the message **Vanish**, it disappears. All done! Have fun helping Scratch Cat rescue those monkeys!

This block runs any script below it when it receives the message vanish

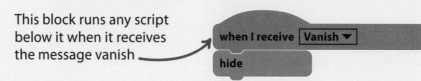

Show what you know

Will you fly through this quiz… or will you need rescuing?

1. Circle the correct answers.

Press the space bar and the cat moves **up / down**. This means the sprite's **x coordinate / y coordinate** value will have **increased / decreased**.

2. Lives is set to 5. What's the value of **Lives** if these blocks are run?

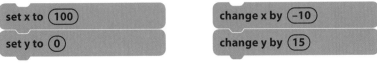

2a. `change Lives ▼ by (-1)`   Value of lives is now..............

2b. `change Lives ▼ by (5)`   Value of lives is now..............

2c. `change Lives ▼ by ( (1) - (2) )`   Value of lives is now..............

3. What would happen if the Buildings sprite's script used the **next costume** block instead of **switch costume to pick random 1 to 10**?

`switch costume to (pick random (1) to (10))` ✗   `next costume` ✓

....

4. If a sprite starts at position (50, 50), where will it be after these blocks of code are run?

`set x to (100)`
`set y to (0)`

`change x by (-10)`
`change y by (15)`

`repeat (10)`
`  change x by (-2)`
`  change y by (5)`

a. (.............. , ...)   **b.** (.............. , ...)   **c.** (.............. , ...)

5. Making Flying Scratch change costumes all the time probably makes the game harder. How could you solve this problem?

....

6. The Buildings sprite's costume "building-h" is so high it's very difficult to rescue the monkey. What change might fix this?

....

7. Challenge! Change the cloud's code to make the clouds move more quickly across the stage every time you rescue a monkey.

Memory Master

Put your memory to the test with this mind-bending musical game! What is the longest sequence of sounds you can remember? Compete with your friends to see who's the Memory Master!

The number of sounds goes up by one with each level, so **Level 7** has seven sounds to remember

Scratch plays a sequence of sounds on these instruments

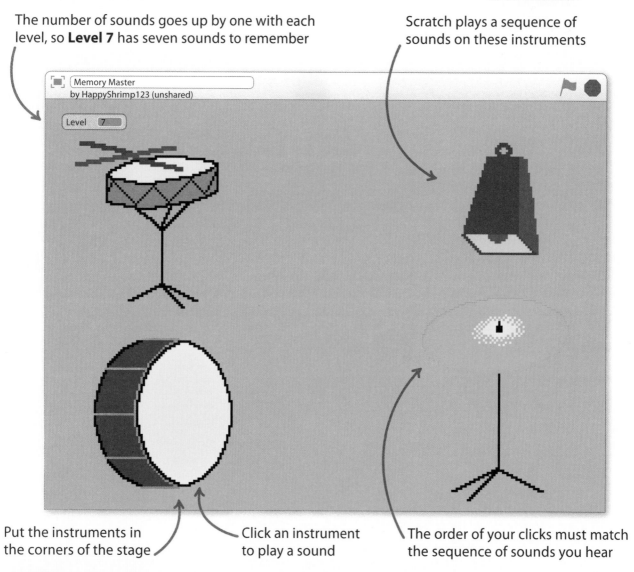

Level   7

Memory Master
by HappyShrimp123 (unshared)

Put the instruments in the corners of the stage

Click an instrument to play a sound

The order of your clicks must match the sequence of sounds you hear

▲ What you do

When you click the flag, you will hear a sequence of sounds played on the instruments. Listen carefully, then click the instruments to repeat the order correctly and progress to the next level. Be on your guard—the sequence gets longer each time, and a single mistake ends the game!

Instructions and backdrops

To begin, we'll add a nice backdrop for the instruments, create a "Game Over!" backdrop for the end of the game, and make an instructions sprite to tell players what to do.

Dig my crazy rhythm!

1 Start a new project and call it "Memory Master." Delete Scratch Cat, then go to the stage info area, and load "purple" from the **Backdrop Library**. Rename it "Start."

2 Next, duplicate the Start backdrop and rename it "Game Over!" Use the **Text** tool (**T**) in the paint editor to type "GAME OVER!" onto the backdrop. Change the font or resize the text with the **Select** tool if you need to. This is the same as what you did in Steps 2–4 of Keepy-Uppy (see page 71).

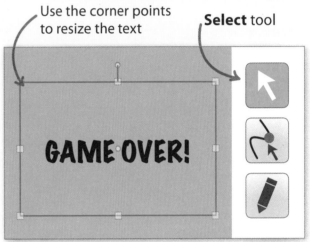

Use the corner points to resize the text

Select tool

GAME OVER!

3 Now go to the sprite list and click on the paintbrush symbol to create a new sprite. Call it "Instructions." In the paint editor, choose black from the palette, select the **Text** tool (**T**), and type out the instructions exactly as shown on the right.

Listen to the sounds. Click the instruments to repeat the sounds in the correct order.

The sequence starts with one sound, but it gets longer each time. Make a mistake and it's "Game Over!"

Press the space bar to start the game.

4 Use the **Select** tool to move the text so it appears in the middle of the stage (the instruments will be in the four corners). You can resize it later if necessary.

5 Add this script to the Instructions sprite. When the flag is clicked, it will show the instructions on the stage at the start of the game. When you press the space bar, the instructions will disappear.

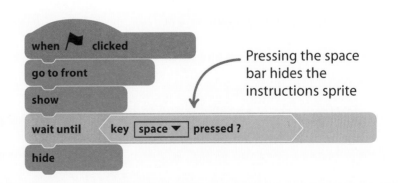

Pressing the space bar hides the instructions sprite

Lists help us remember!

Next, we need to make some variables, and also a list. The list will keep a record of the number and order of sounds that the instruments play.

6 Under the **Data** tab, select **Make a variable**. Type "**Checker**" as the variable's name and click **OK**. Make three more variables. Call them "**Counter**," "**Level**," and "**Random**." All of their check boxes should be left unchecked, except for the one next to **Level**.

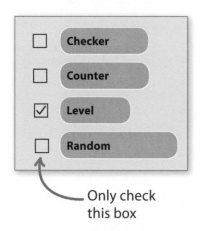

Only check this box

7 Below the **Make a Variable** button under the **Data** tab, you'll see another button called **Make a List**. Select that and type "**Sound list**" in the pop-up box's window. Click **OK**. When it appears under the **Data** blocks, uncheck its check box.

New List	
List name:	Sound list

● For all sprites   ○ For this sprite only

OK   Cancel

Lists

Making a list is a great way to store a set of information, such as numbers or words. Lots of programming languages use lists. They are handy for all sorts of things, from creating leaderboards and doing complex calculations to giving sprites artificial intelligence, so they look like they make their own decisions. In Memory Master, we use a list to store the sounds made by our musical instruments.

You can use a list to make a sprite say something random when you click on it

Lists are usually hidden, but you can display them on the stage just like variables

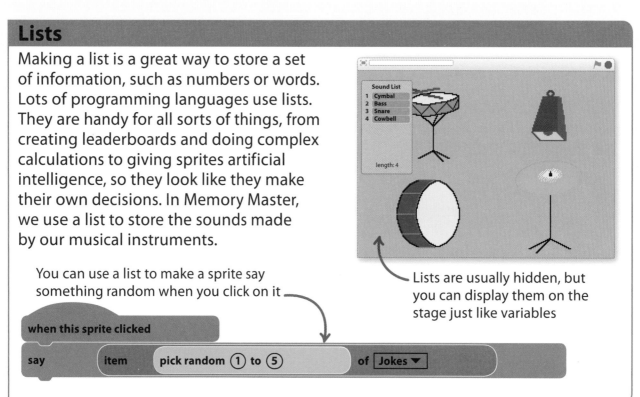

Adding the instruments

There are four instruments in the Scratch percussion orchestra, so lets load them into the project and give them some scripts.

8 First, load the big bass drum ("Drum-Bass") from the **Sprite Library**. It has three sounds.

Drum-Bass

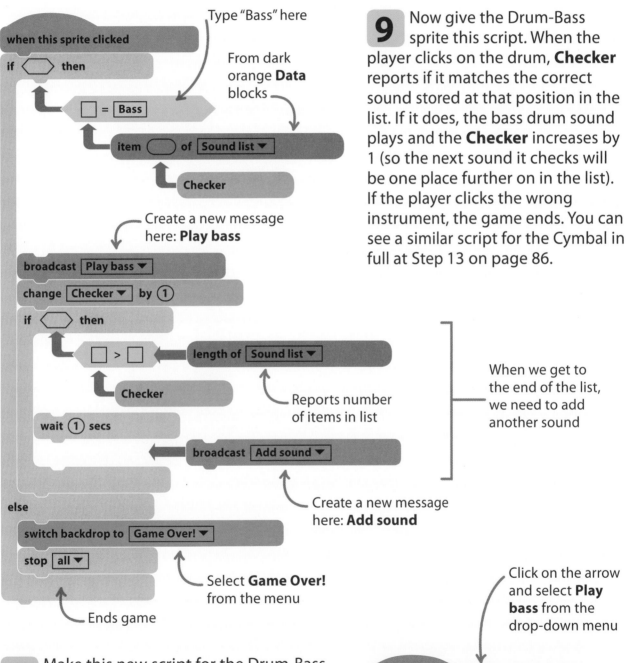

Type "Bass" here

From dark orange **Data** blocks

```
when this sprite clicked
if <  > then
        [ ] = [Bass]
             item (  ) of [Sound list ▼]
                  Checker
```

Create a new message here: **Play bass**

```
broadcast [Play bass ▼]
change [Checker ▼] by (1)
if <  > then
        [ ] > [ ]    length of [Sound list ▼]
             Checker
        wait (1) secs
                    broadcast [Add sound ▼]
else
    switch backdrop to [Game Over! ▼]
    stop [all ▼]
```

Reports number of items in list

When we get to the end of the list, we need to add another sound

Create a new message here: **Add sound**

Select **Game Over!** from the menu

Ends game

9 Now give the Drum-Bass sprite this script. When the player clicks on the drum, **Checker** reports if it matches the correct sound stored at that position in the list. If it does, the bass drum sound plays and the **Checker** increases by 1 (so the next sound it checks will be one place further on in the list). If the player clicks the wrong instrument, the game ends. You can see a similar script for the Cymbal in full at Step 13 on page 86.

10 Make this new script for the Drum-Bass sprite. When it receives the **Play bass** message, it will play whichever of the sprite's sounds you have selected in the window of the **play sound** block.

Click on the arrow and select **Play bass** from the drop-down menu

```
when I receive [Play bass ▼]
play sound [drum bass3 ▼]
```

Choose the drum sound you like best. Click on the pink block to hear sound

11 Now load these three new sprites from the **Sprite Library**: "Cymbal," "Cowbell," and "Drum-Snare." Put the four instruments in the corners of the stage.

Cymbal

Cowbell

Drum-Snare

12 Add the same scripts you built for the Drum-Bass sprite to each of the new sprites. The easiest way is to click, drag, and drop the scripts from one sprite onto another. This will copy the scripts to the new sprite.

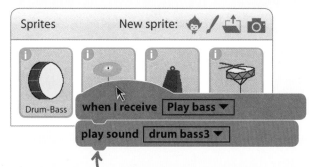

Sprites   New sprite:

Drum-Bass

when I receive Play bass ▼

play sound drum bass3 ▼

Release the mouse when the pointer is over the sprite you want to copy the code to

13 Create a new message for each instrument sprite. For example, for the cymbal click on the **broadcast** block's arrow and select **new message**. Type "**Play cymbal**" into the pop-up window and click **OK**. Also change "Bass" to "Cymbal" in the window of the green **add** block.

Change the name here to "Cymbal." Use "Cowbell" and "Snare" for the other two instruments

when this sprite clicked

if ⟨ item Checker of Sound list ▼ = Cymbal ⟩ then

    broadcast Play cymbal ▼

    change Checker ▼ by ①

    if ⟨ Checker > length of Sound list ▼ ⟩ then

        wait ① secs

        broadcast Add sound ▼

else

    switch backdrop to Game Over! ▼

    stop all ▼

Add a new message for each instrument sprite

14 For each instrument, select the correct message in the window of the **when I receive** block, and choose a sound in the **play sound** block.

Select the correct message here

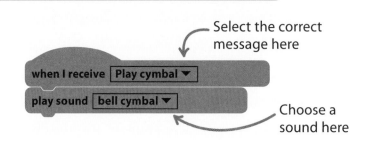

when I receive Play cymbal ▼

play sound bell cymbal ▼

Choose a sound here

Scripting the list

In the stage's scripts area, we'll build the code for creating the list, playing it back, and clearing it before each new game.

Select **all** from the menu

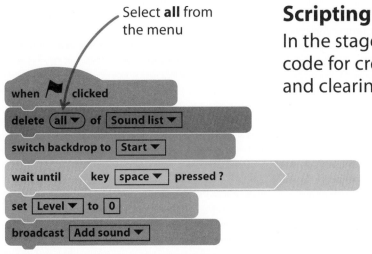

```
when 🏴 clicked
delete (all ▼) of [Sound list ▼]
switch backdrop to [Start ▼]
wait until   < key [space ▼] pressed ? >
set [Level ▼] to [0]
broadcast [Add sound ▼]
```

15 Click on the stage info area and add this script. Clicking the flag clears the information stored in the list from the last game. Pressing the space bar starts a new game.

16 Add this code to the stage. It numbers the instrument sounds from 1 to 4. When it receives the **Add sound** message, it picks a random number from 1 to 4 and adds that sound to the list of sounds to be played. Then it broadcasts the message **Play sound list**, which you'll have to create in a **broadcast** block.

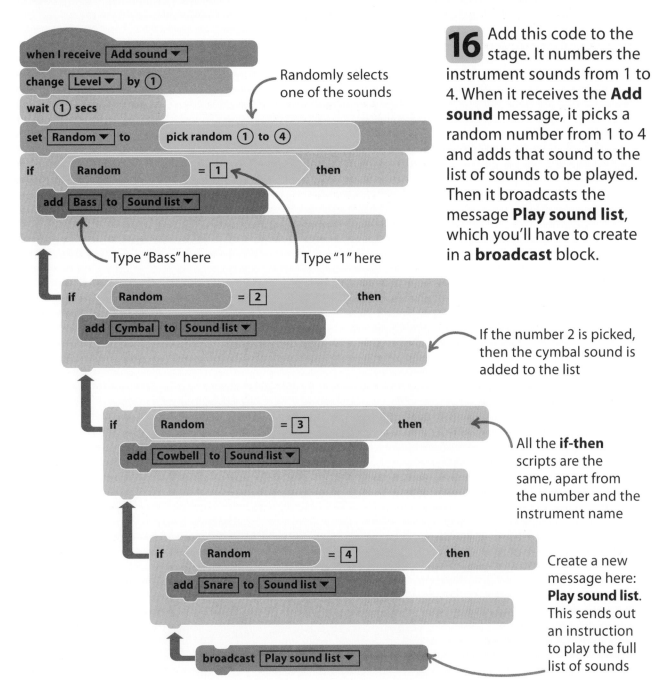

Randomly selects one of the sounds

Type "Bass" here

Type "1" here

If the number 2 is picked, then the cymbal sound is added to the list

All the **if-then** scripts are the same, apart from the number and the instrument name

Create a new message here: **Play sound list**. This sends out an instruction to play the full list of sounds

17 Now give the stage this third and final script. When it receives the **Play sound list** message, the script uses the **Counter** variable to play all the sounds in the order they were added to the list.

Click and select message

Counter keeps track as the script works down the list, starting with the first sound

List stops playing when the value of the variable **Counter** is greater than number of sounds in the list

Script plays whichever sound is first in the list

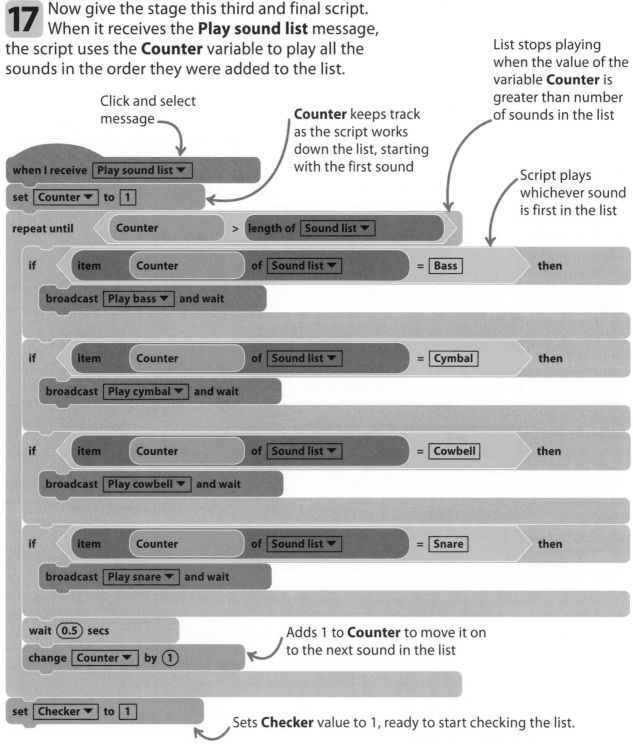

```
when I receive [Play sound list ▼]
set [Counter ▼] to [1]
repeat until < Counter > length of [Sound list ▼] >
    if < item (Counter) of [Sound list ▼] = [Bass] > then
        broadcast [Play bass ▼] and wait
    if < item (Counter) of [Sound list ▼] = [Cymbal] > then
        broadcast [Play cymbal ▼] and wait
    if < item (Counter) of [Sound list ▼] = [Cowbell] > then
        broadcast [Play cowbell ▼] and wait
    if < item (Counter) of [Sound list ▼] = [Snare] > then
        broadcast [Play snare ▼] and wait
    wait (0.5) secs
    change [Counter ▼] by (1)
set [Checker ▼] to [1]
```

Adds 1 to **Counter** to move it on to the next sound in the list

Sets **Checker** value to 1, ready to start checking the list.

18 Run the project. The code is complicated, so check that the project's working as it should. If something's not right, look closely at every script to make sure there are no mistakes. You may want to resize the text and move the instruments so that the instructions are easy to read. When everything's OK, start playing!

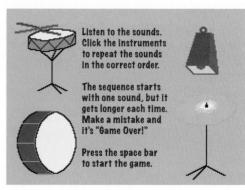

Listen to the sounds. Click the instruments to repeat the sounds in the correct order.

The sequence starts with one sound, but it gets longer each time. Make a mistake and it's "Game Over!"

Press the space bar to start the game.

Show what you know
Are you a Scratch Master as well as a Memory Master? Find out!

1. Circle the correct answers.

1a. The **counter / checker** variable is used when the program plays through the sequence of sounds in the list.

1b. The **counter / checker** variable is used when the player clicks an instrument.

2. The check box next to **Sound list** under the **Data** tab is unchecked. Why is this necessary?

....

....

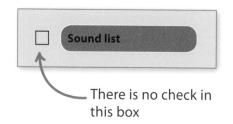

There is no check in this box

3. Draw lines to link these list blocks to their correct descriptions.

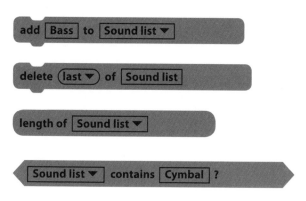

Reports the number of items in the list

Reports "True" if it finds "Cymbal" in the list

Removes the item at the end of the list

Inserts "Bass" at the end of the list

4. Bug hunt! There are three mistakes, or bugs, in this script for the stage. Can you find them? Circle the errors.

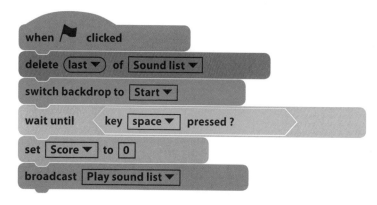

5. Challenge! Make Memory Master even more challenging by adding an extra instrument, the "Drum-Tabla," to the game. Change the scripts to handle five instruments.

Load this sprite from the library

Drum-Tabla

How to Build Tropical Tunes

Computer games aren't just about quick reflexes —they can also challenge your thinking powers. Here's a brain game to test how good your memory is.

Aim of the game

In Tropical Tunes, you have to listen to the drums play and then repeat the ever-growing tune. Make a mistake and the game's over. The longer you can match the tune, the higher your score.

 ◀ **Listen**
The drums play a tune, starting with a single note and then adding one new note each time.

 ◀ **Drums**
Click the drums in order to repeat the tune the game plays to you.

 ◀ **Game over**
Make a mistake and the game ends. As the tune gets longer, the game gets harder.

Click this icon to make the game fill your screen.

You score a point each time you click on the correct drum.

Tropical Tunes
by CrazyDrummer123 (unshared)

Score   0

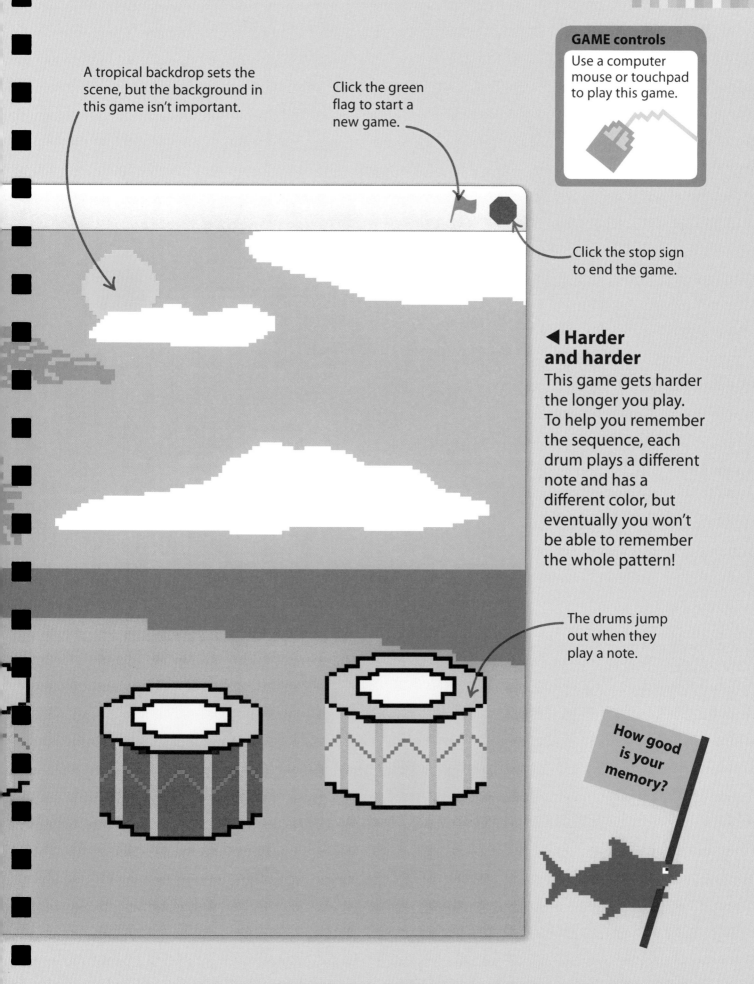

A tropical backdrop sets the scene, but the background in this game isn't important.

Click the green flag to start a new game.

GAME controls

Use a computer mouse or touchpad to play this game.

Click the stop sign to end the game.

◀ Harder and harder

This game gets harder the longer you play. To help you remember the sequence, each drum plays a different note and has a different color, but eventually you won't be able to remember the whole pattern!

The drums jump out when they play a note.

How good is your memory?

Make a drum

This game is quite complicated, so you'll need to work through the instructions carefully. To get started, follow the directions to make one drum with all the scripts it needs. Once that's done you can copy it to make all four drums. Later, you'll create a game loop called the "master controller" to play the drums.

Give the game a title.

1 Create a new Scratch project and add or create any backdrop you want. A tropical theme works well with this game.

Tropical Tunes
by CrazyDrummer123 (unshared)

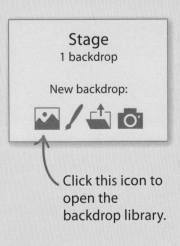

Stage
1 backdrop

New backdrop:

Click this icon to open the backdrop library.

2 The game needs four drums, but you can make just one to start with. Delete the cat sprite and add the "Drum1" sprite from the sprite library. Drag it to the lower left of the stage.

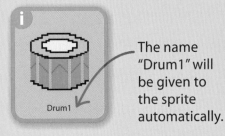

Drum1

The name "Drum1" will be given to the sprite automatically.

Variables

Programmers have special terms for variables that apply to all sprites or only one sprite.

▶ Those that apply to only one sprite are called **local variables**.

▶ Those that apply to all sprites are called **global variables**.

Two types of variable

You may have noticed the option to choose "For all sprites" or "For this sprite only" when you create a variable. So far you've mostly used "For all sprites", but you'll need to use both options in this game.

3 Before you can start making the scripts that bring the drum to life, you need to create some variables. Click on the Data section and make two variables for all sprites called "DrumToPlay" and "ClickedDrum". Uncheck their boxes. Every sprite in the game can use these variables.

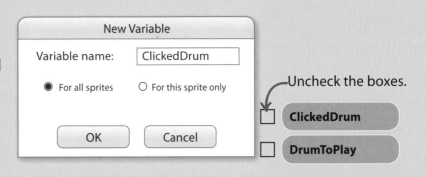

Uncheck the boxes.

4 Now add three variables "For this sprite only". Call them "drumColor", "drumNote", and "drumNumber". These variables will store information about only Drum1: its number, its color, and which note it plays. Using "For this sprite only" enables you to copy this sprite to make more drums later, while allowing each drum to have different values for these variables.

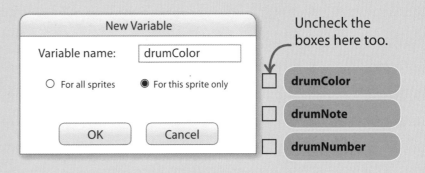

Uncheck the boxes here too.

5 Build the script below for Drum1. It sets up the drum's number, color, the note it plays, and the type of sound it makes (like a steel drum). Run the project to set the variables and watch the drum change color.

This drum's variable information is set up in these three blocks.

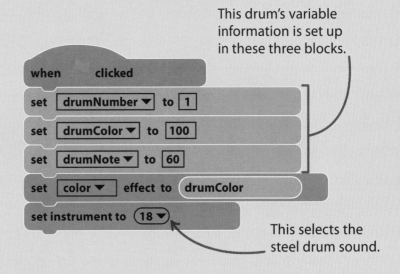

This selects the steel drum sound.

Making your own block

To avoid repeating the same set of blocks over and over again, it's possible to create new blocks which each contain several different instructions. You'll need to create a few customized Scratch blocks in this game.

6 Go to the blocks palette and select "More Blocks". The option "Make a Block" will be visible.

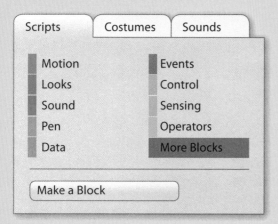

7 Select "Make a Block" and a box will pop up. Type in the name of your new block: "play drum". Then click "OK".

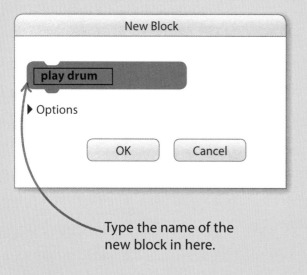

Type the name of the new block in here.

8 Next, the new block appears in the blocks palette and a special purple header block, "define play drum", appears in the scripts area.

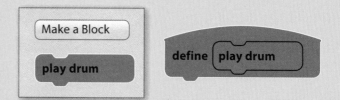

9 Build this script below the "define play drum" block. Then, anywhere you use the "play drum" block, Scratch will run the script. The script will make the drum grow in size, play a note, and then shrink back to normal. You can test the new "play drum" block by clicking on it.

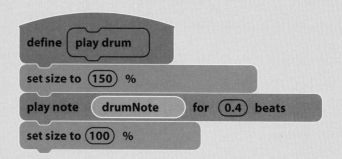

10 Now add this short script to Drum1. Click the drum on the stage to test it. Before testing, you'll need to click the green flag to set the value of drumNote.

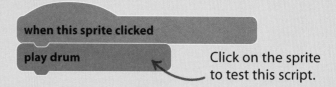

Click on the sprite to test this script.

Remote control drums

Tropical Tunes makes the drums play a sequence that the player has to copy. The game controls the drums by using a master controller to send messages to them and then wait for a reply. Before you set up the master controller, give Drum1 the scripts it needs to receive and broadcast messages.

11 Build this script, which will be triggered by a message called "RemoteControl". Create the message by selecting the drop-down menu on the "when I receive" block. Choose "new message" and type in "RemoteControl".

Create a new message called "RemoteControl".

```
when I receive  RemoteControl ▼

if       DrumToPlay  =  drumNumber       then

    play drum
```

▼How it works

Eventually there will be four drums numbered 1 to 4 (the local variable drumNumber). Before the master controller broadcasts "RemoteControl" it will set the *global* variable "DrumToPlay" to the number of the drum it wants to sound, and only the matching drum will play. We will add these steps later.

This variable for all sprites tells the game which drum to play.

```
set  DrumToPlay ▼  to  2

broadcast   RemoteControl ▼  and wait
```

Don't add these blocks yet— we'll use them later.

MESSAGE

Only Drum2 plays, because its "drumNumber" matches "DrumToPlay".

IGNORES   PLAYS   IGNORES   IGNORES

Drum1   Drum2   Drum3   Drum4

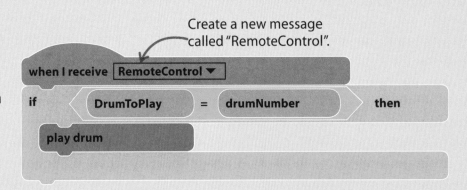

12 When the player clicks a drum, the master controller will need to check it's the right one. To make this work, you need to make the clicked drum do two things. First, it will change the global variable "ClickedDrum" to its own number. Then it will broadcast a message to make the master controller run its check. Change Drum1's "when this sprite clicked" script to look like this.

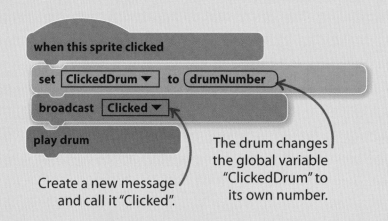

The drum changes the global variable "ClickedDrum" to its own number.

Create a new message and call it "Clicked".

Four drums

You now have one drum complete with its scripts. You can copy it three times to create the four drums you need for this game.

13 Duplicate the drum three times, then change the values of the three local variables as shown below to give each drum a different number, color, and note. Arrange the drums on the stage, ordered from one to four.

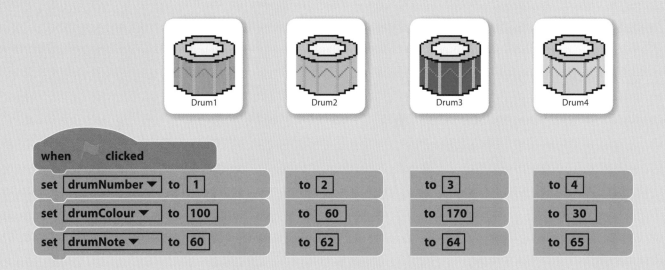

14 Now run the project. Each drum should become a different colour. Click on them in turn to hear them play. If they move instead of playing, click on the blue full-screen symbol in the top left of the stage. Nothing else will work yet, but it's good to test that your drums all play correctly.

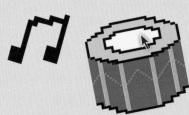

The master controller

Now you need to create the game's main brain: the master controller. The master controller broadcasts the "RemoteControl" message that plays the drums, but it does several other jobs too. It generates the drumbeat sequence the player has to follow; it checks that the player has clicked the right drum; and it keeps track of the score. It will need several scripts to do all this.

15 The stage is a good place to put the master controller scripts as they don't belong to any one sprite. Click on the stage info area at the bottom left of the screen to choose the stage.

Stage
1 backdrop

New backdrop:

Click here to add scripts to the stage.

16 The master controller will keep track of the ever-growing sequence of drumbeats by storing them in a numbered list. To create the list, open the Data blocks section and click the "Make a List" button. Name it "DrumOrder"—it's going to store the order in which the drums will play. Check the box so you can see it on the stage.

New List

List name: DrumOrder

● For all sprites

OK   Cancel

Check here to show the list on the stage.

Make a list

☑ **DrumOrder**

17 With the stage selected, build this test script to generate a random sequence of seven drum numbers in the list. This script isn't part of the final game (for that, the script will need to add notes one by one). However, building it will show you how lists work and will let you try out the drums.

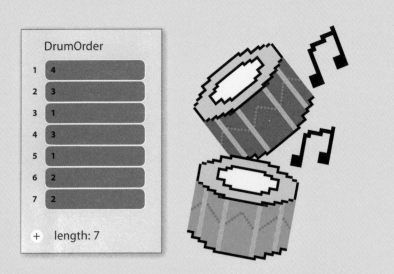

```
when       clicked
delete ( all ▼ ) of  DrumOrder ▼
repeat (7)
    add  pick random (1) to (4)  to  DrumOrder ▼
    wait (1) sec
```

This block clears the list at the start of the test.

This block adds a random drum number to the end of the list.

The "wait" block gives you time to see what's going on.

18 Run the script and watch the "DrumOrder" list on the stage slowly fill up. It will look like this, but your numbers won't be the same. The drums don't play yet because there are no blocks to tell them to.

DrumOrder

1	4
2	3
3	1
4	3
5	1
6	2
7	2

+   length: 7

Lists

Making a list is a great way to store information, and lots of programming languages use them. They are handy for all sorts of things, from creating leaderboards and doing complex calculations to giving sprites artificial intelligence. In Tropical Tunes, we use a list to store numbers, but you can store words in lists too.

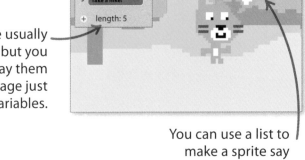

Cat Cruncher
by GreenDino99

Insults
1 You're so dumb.
2 I hate you!
3 What's that smell?
4 Make like a tree!
5 Take a hike!

+   length: 5

Take a hike!

Lists are usually hidden, but you can display them on the stage just like variables.

You can use a list to make a sprite say something random when you click on it.

```
when this sprite clicked
say   item  pick random (1) to (5)  of  Insults ▼
```

Commanding the drums

19 Now create another new block called "play sequence" and build the script shown here. It will play the notes in the list in order by travelling once though the blocks in the loop for each item in the "DrumOrder" list, setting "DrumToPlay" from the list, and then sending out the "RemoteControl" message. You will need to create a new variable for all sprites called "Count".

The "Count" variable keeps track as the program works down the list.

This block puts the drum's number in the "DrumtoPlay" variable.

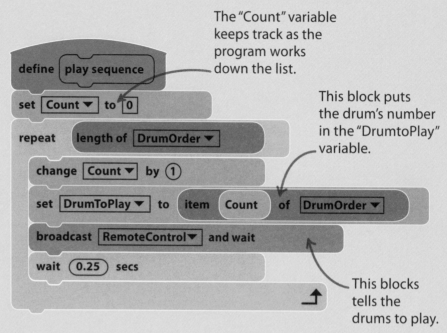

This blocks tells the drums to play.

20 Add the new "play sequence" block to the test script.

Place the new "play sequence" block here.

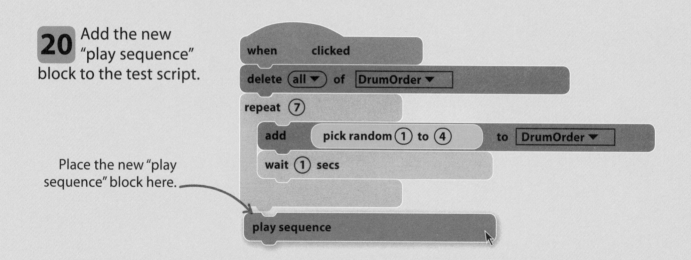

Broadcast blocks

There are two types of broadcast Scratch blocks. They are useful in different ways.

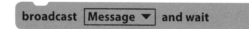

▲ Broadcast
This sends the message but then continues straight to the next block without waiting. This is useful for triggering an event without stopping what's going on, such as launching an arrow without pausing the loop that moves the player's sprite.

▲ Broadcast and wait
This sends the message but then waits until all receiving scripts have finished before running the next block. This is useful when you don't want the script to continue until something's finished, such as the drum playing in this game.

21 Now run the script. Watch the numbers alongside the items in "DrumOrder" light up as they are read by the script, then hear and see the correct drum play each time. You can check the "DrumToPlay" variable's check box to show the number used with the "Remote Control" message for each note.

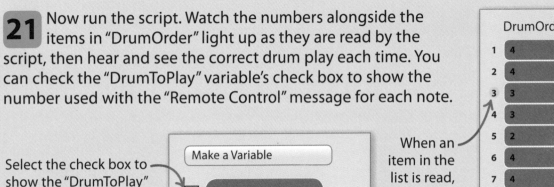

Select the check box to show the "DrumToPlay" variable on screen.

When an item in the list is read, its index number flashes.

Adding notes to the tune

So far you've just been testing the drums. It's now time to get them playing the sequences needed in the game, starting with one note and adding another note each time the player repeats the tune correctly.

22 The test script isn't needed any more so replace it with this one. You'll need to create another new block called "wait for player"—its script is shown in the next step. You'll also need to create a new variable for all sprites, called "Score", and check it so it appears on the stage.

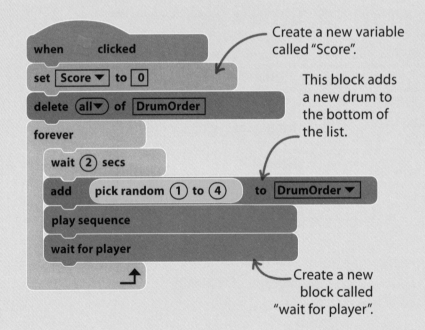

Create a new variable called "Score".

This block adds a new drum to the bottom of the list.

Create a new block called "wait for player".

23 Add a new variable called "CorrectCount" to count how many drums the player gets right. Then create this script, which holds up the loop while it waits for the player to get the whole drum sequence right.

24 If you run the project now, the drums will play one note and then wait. You can click as many drums as you like but nothing will happen because you haven't programmed the master controller to respond to the "Clicked" message yet.

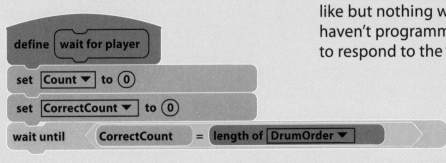

Checking the player's tune

Now you need to add a script to respond to the player's clicks on the drums. Every click creates a "Clicked" message that can trigger a script to check which drum was clicked and count the number of correct clicks. If the player clicks the wrong drum, the script will broadcast a "GameOver" message.

25 Add the next script to the stage to increase "CorrectCount" by one for each correct click. When the drums are clicked, they play and send the "Clicked" message, having put their number in "ClickedDrum". This script will be triggered by that "Clicked" message. If the numbers don't match, the game ends.

This is the number of the correct drum held in the list.

This is the number of the drum you clicked.

Create a new message called "GameOver".

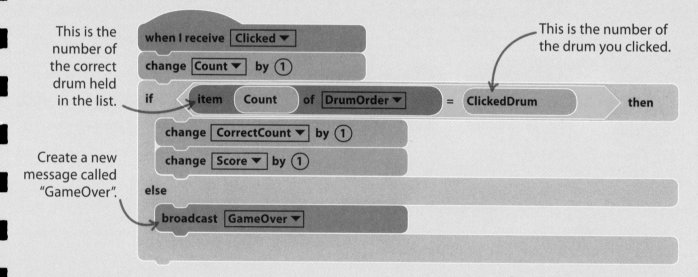

```
when I receive Clicked ▼
change Count ▼ by 1
if     item  Count  of DrumOrder ▼  = ClickedDrum  then
    change CorrectCount ▼ by 1
    change Score ▼ by 1
else
    broadcast GameOver ▼
```

26 Add a game-over script to the stage. You'll need to load the "bell toll" sound to the stage from the Scratch sound library.

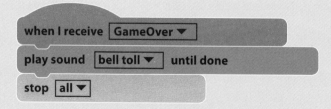

```
when I receive GameOver ▼
play sound bell toll ▼ until done
stop all ▼
```

27 The game is complete. Now try playing it, but remember to uncheck "DrumOrder" in the Data section of the blocks palette or the player can just read the correct drum order off the list.

Uncheck the box to hide the drum order from the player.

```
Make a List
☐ DrumOrder
```

▶ How it works

This game relies on two messages: "RemoteControl", which tells a drum to play, and "Clicked", which tells the master controller that a drum has been clicked by the player. The master controller has a loop that uses these two messages in turn —to play the tune and then check the player's reaction.

The master controller loops through these three actions.

Master controller
Adds note to sequence
Plays sequence
Waits for player to click sequence

 "RemoteControl" message makes the drums play.

 "Clicked" message tells the master controller when a drum is clicked.

 Drum1

 Drum2

 Drum3

 Drum4

Hacks and tweaks

Once everything is working smoothly, you can play around with the code and tweak the game to try and make it more exciting or harder. Here are some ideas.

Obey me!

▲ Talking shark
Try adding a shark sprite that swims up and gives instructions —make him talk using the "say" block.

14

▲ Round counter
Create a new global variable "Round" and show it on the stage. Set it to zero at the start of a game and increase it by one every time the player completes a sequence correctly (at the end of the master controller loop).

▼ Another drum
Add a fifth drum. You'll need to change its drum number, note, and color values, and check anywhere in the code that thinks there are only four drums —such as the random block in the master controller.

GAME OVER!

◀ Game over
Add a game-over sign or make the shark swim back onto the stage to say it.

Debugging

Bugs are errors in programs. Getting rid of them is called debugging. If a program isn't working properly, there are a number of common Scratch problems you can check for, which are shown below. If you're following instructions and something isn't working, it's also worth going back to the beginning and checking all the steps—there could be a small mistake in one of your scripts that is affecting the whole game.

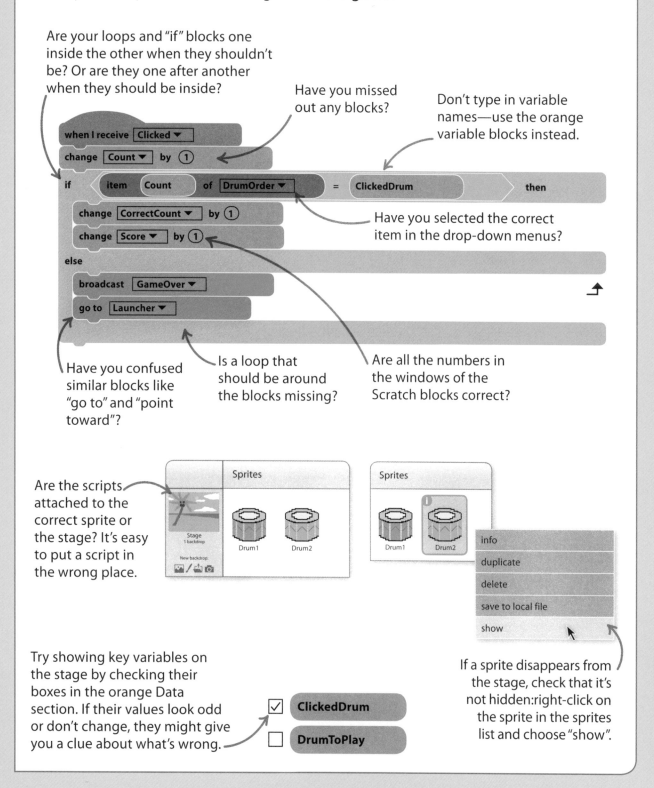

Are your loops and "if" blocks one inside the other when they shouldn't be? Or are they one after another when they should be inside?

Have you missed out any blocks?

Don't type in variable names—use the orange variable blocks instead.

Have you selected the correct item in the drop-down menus?

Have you confused similar blocks like "go to" and "point toward"?

Is a loop that should be around the blocks missing?

Are all the numbers in the windows of the Scratch blocks correct?

Are the scripts attached to the correct sprite or the stage? It's easy to put a script in the wrong place.

Try showing key variables on the stage by checking their boxes in the orange Data section. If their values look odd or don't change, they might give you a clue about what's wrong.

If a sprite disappears from the stage, check that it's not hidden:right-click on the sprite in the sprites list and choose "show".

Better Scratch

Good programmers try to write code that's easy to understand and change. There are many ways in which you can improve your projects and expand your knowledge of Scratch. Here are a few of them.

▲ Use clear names

Scratch lets you choose names for sprites, variables, and messages. Make sure you use meaningful names, such as "Dragon" or "Score", to make your Scratch code readable.

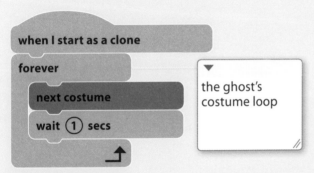

the ghost's costume loop

▲ Comments

You can add comments to any block to explain your code. To do this, right-click (control click on a Mac) on it and select "Add comment". This can remind you when you read code written a while ago.

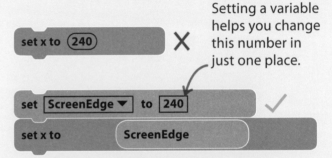

Setting a variable helps you change this number in just one place.

▲ No unexplained numbers

Avoid writing code that contains unexplained numbers. To make your code easier to read, add a comment or use a variable so the number explains itself.

▼ Backpack

The backpack is a feature found at the bottom of the Scratch screen. It lets you store useful scripts, sprites, sounds, and costumes and move them from project to project. But remember that you can only use it online.

Drag and drop a script or sprite to copy it to the backpack.

Backpack

Sound Scream-female

Costume monkey2-a

Backdrop Underwater2

Script

The help tool

Are you still unsure about how to use certain blocks? The help tool in Scratch will let you master the function of each block with ease.

1 To find out more about a particular block, first click the "Block help" symbol in the toolbar at the top of the screen.

"Block help" symbol

2 After the mouse-pointer turns into a question mark, click on any block in the blocks palette. A help window opens with tips on how to use that block.

if on edge, bounce

?

The mouse-pointer turns into a question mark.

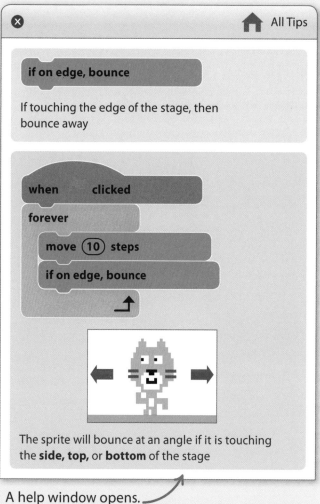

A help window opens.

Making your project different

Scratch projects often look and sound similar if you only use resources from the Scratch library. To make yours different, import your own images and sounds into Scratch.

Click here to upload an image file from your computer.

Click here to use your webcam to take a picture.

Use this to record sounds.

Click here to use a sound file from your computer.

▲ **Your own images**
You can import any image into Scratch, but don't share a project containing photos of people you know. You can also create your own images with a graphics program or the paint editor in Scratch.

▲ **Your own sounds**
You can record your own music and sound effects through your computer's microphone and edit them in Scratch. You can also find free music and sounds on the web to use in your games.

Bad Programs

Not all programs are fun games or useful apps. Some programs are designed to steal your data or damage your computer. They will often seem harmless, and you might not realize that you have been a victim.

Malware

Programs that do things without your knowledge or permission are known as "malware". Unauthorized access to a computer is a crime, but there are many different types of programs that still try to sneak on to your computer.

▶ Worm

A worm is a type of malware that crawls around a network from computer to computer. Worms can clog up networks, slowing them down —the first worm brought the Internet to a virtual standstill in 1988.

▲ Virus

Just like a virus in the human body, this malware copies itself over and over again. They are usually spread through emails, USB sticks, or other methods of transferring files between computers.

▲ Trojan

Malware that pretends to be a harmless program is known as a "trojan". The word comes from a ruse used in the Trojan War: the Greeks gave the Trojans a giant wooden horse, with soldiers hidden inside. By breaching the Trojan defenses without detection, they won the war.

Famous worm

On May 5, 2000, Internet users in the Philippines received emails with the subject "ILOVEYOU". An attachment appeared to be a love letter, but was actually a piece of malware that corrupted files.

◀ ILOVEYOU

This worm quickly spread to computers around the world. It is estimated to have cost more than $20 billion to fix the damage it caused.

What malware does

Viruses, worms, and trojans are all types of malware that are created to get into your machine, but what do they do once they have infected their target? They might delete or corrupt files, steal passwords, or seek to control your machine for some larger purpose as part of an organized "zombie botnet".

▶ Zombie botnets

Botnets are collections of infected computers that can be used to send spam emails, or flood a target website with traffic to bring it crashing down.

Good software to the rescue

Thankfully, people aren't defenseless in the fight against malware. Anti-malware software has become big business, with many providers competing to provide the best protection. Two well-known examples are firewalls and antivirus programs.

▲ Antivirus programs

Antivirus software tries to detect malware. It identifies bad programs by scanning files and comparing their contents with a database of suspicious code.

▲ Firewalls

Firewalls aim to prevent malware and dangerous network traffic from reaching your computer. They scan all incoming data from the Internet.

Hackers

Coders that study and write malware are known as "hackers". Those who write malware to commit crimes are known as "black-hat" hackers, and those who write programs to try to protect against malware are known as "white-hat" hackers.

White-hat hacker   Black-hat hacker

Become a Master Programmer

The secret to becoming a master programmer is to have fun. As long as you're enjoying yourself, there's no limit to how skilled you can become at coding, whether as a hobby or a lifelong career.

Ways to become a better programmer

Like skiing, learning the piano, or playing tennis, coding is a skill that you'll get better and better at over time. It can take years to become a true expert, but if you're having fun on the way, it will feel like an effortless journey. Here are a few tips to help you become a master programmer.

▲ Code a lot

People say practice makes perfect—and it's true. The more code you write, the better you'll get. Keep going and you'll soon be an expert.

◀ Be nosy

Read websites and books about programming and try out other people's code. You'll pick up expert tips and tricks that might have taken you years to figure out on your own.

▲ Steal ideas

If you come across a great program, think how you might code it yourself. Look for clever ideas to use in your own code. All the best programmers copy each other's ideas and try to improve them.

▶ Show a friend

Teach someone else to code and you'll learn a lot yourself. Explaining how coding works is a great way of making sure you understand it thoroughly.

▶ Train your brain

Your brain is like a muscle— if you exercise it, it will get stronger. Do things that help you think like a programmer. Solve logic puzzles and brainteasers, take up Sudoku, and work on your math.

▶ Test your code

Test your code by entering crazy values to see what happens. See how well it stands up to errors. Try rewriting it to improve it or try rewriting someone else's—you'll learn all their secret tricks.

Scala **Pascal** SQL
Ruby on rails C++

◀ Build a robot army

You can connect your computer to all sorts of programmable devices, from flashing LED lights to robots. It's fun and you'll learn lots as you figure out how to conquer the world.

▲ Learn new languages

Become multilingual. Every new programming language you learn will teach you more about the ones you already know (or *thought* you knew). You can download free versions of most languages.

▶ Pull a computer to bits

Take an old computer apart to see how it works (ask permission first!). There aren't many components, so it won't take long to figure out what all the bits are. Best of all, build your own computer and then run your code on it.

▶ Win a prize

When your skills develop, why not enter an online coding contest? There are lots to choose from at all different levels. The toughest are worldwide competitions like Google's Code Jam, but there are easier challenges too.

Have fun!

Coding is a lot like trying to solve puzzles. It's challenging and you'll often get stuck. Sometimes it's frustrating. But you'll also have breakthroughs when you solve a problem and feel a buzz of excitement at seeing your code work. The best way to keeping coding fun is to take on challenges that suit you. If a project is too easy you'll get bored; if it's too hard you'll lose interest. Never be afraid to fiddle, tinker, experiment, and break the rules—let your curiosity lead you. But most of all, remember to have fun!

Glossary

algorithm
A set of step-by-step instructions followed when performing a task: for example, by a computer program.

ASCII
"American Standard Code for Information Interchange"—a code used for storing text characters as binary code.

binary code
A way of writing numbers and data that uses only 0s and 1s.

bit
A binary digit—0 or 1. The smallest unit of digital information.

Boolean expression
A question that has only two possible answers, such as "true" and "false".

branch
A point in a program where two different options are available to choose from.

bug
An error in a program's code that makes it behave in an unexpected way

byte
A unit of digital information that contains eight bits.

call
To use a function in a program.

compression
A way of making data smaller so that it takes up less storage space.

computer network
A way to link two or more computers together.

container
A part of a program that can be used to store a number of other data items.

data
Information, such as text, symbols, and numerical values.

debug
To look for and correct errors in a program.

debugger
A program that checks other programs for errors in their code.

directory
A place to store files to keep them organized.

encryption
A way of encoding data so that only certain people can read or access it.

event
Something a computer program can react to, such as a key being pressed or the mouse being clicked.

execute
See *run*.

file
A collection of data stored with a name.

float
A number with a decimal point in it.

function
A piece of code that does part of a larger task.

gate
Used by computers to make decisions. Gates use one or more input signals to produce an output signal, based on a rule. For example, "AND" gates produce a positive output only when both input signals are positive. Other gates include "OR" and "NOT".

GPU
A graphics processing unit (GPU) allows images to be displayed on a computer screen.

graphics
Visual elements on a screen that are not text, such as pictures, icons, and symbols.

GUI
The GUI, or graphical user interface, is the name for the buttons and windows that make up the part of the program you can see and interact with.

hacker
A person who breaks into a computer system. "White hat" hackers work for computer security companies and look for problems in order to fix them. "Black hat" hackers break into computer systems to cause harm or to make profit from them.

hardware
The physical parts of a computer that you can see or touch, such as wires, the keyboard, and the display screen.

hexadecimal
A number system based on 16, where the numbers 10 to 15 are represented by the letters A to F.

index number
A number given to an item in a list. In Python, the index number of the first item will be 0, the second item 1, and so on.

input
Data that is entered into a computer: for example, from a microphone, keyboard, or mouse.

integer
Any number that does not contain a decimal point and is not written as a fraction (a whole number).

interface
The means by which the user interacts with software or hardware.

IP address
A series of numbers that makes up a computer's individual address when it is connected to the Internet.

library
A collection of functions that can be reused in other projects.

loop
Part of a program that repeats itself (to prevent the need for the same piece of code to be typed out multiple times).

machine code
The basic language understood by computers. Programming languages must be translated into machine code before the processor can read them.

malware
Software that is designed to harm or disrupt a computer. Malware is short for "malicious software".

memory
A computer chip inside a computer that stores data.

module
A section of code that performs a single part of an overall program.

operator
A symbol that performs a specific function: for example, "+" (addition) or "-" (subtraction).

OS
A computer's operating system (OS) provides the basis for other programs to run, and connects them to hardware.

output
Data that is produced by a computer program and viewed by the user.

port
A series of numbers used by a computer as the "address" for a specific program.

processor
A type of electronic chip inside a computer that runs programs.

program
A set of instructions that a computer follows in order to complete a task.

programming language
A language that is used to give instructions to a computer.

random
A function in a computer program that allows unpredictable outcomes. Useful when creating games.

run
The command to make a program start.

server
A computer that stores files accessible via a network.

single-step
A way of making a computer program run one step at a time, to check that each step is working properly.

socket
The combination of an IP address and a port, which lets programs send data directly to each other over the Internet.

software
The programs that run on a computer and control how it works.

sprite
A movable object.

statement
The smallest complete instruction a programming language can be broken down into.

string
A series of characters. Strings can contain numbers, letters, or symbols, such as a colon.

syntax
The rules that determine how a program must be structured in order for it to work properly.

trojan
A piece of malware that pretends to be another piece of software to trick the user.

tuple
A list of items separated by commas and surrounded by brackets.

Unicode
A universal code used by computers to represent thousands of symbols and text characters.

variable
A named place where you can store information that can be changed.

virus
A type of malware that works by multiplying itself to spread between computers.

Solutions

Well done, you've completed all the tasks! Time to check your answers. How did you do? Are you a Scratch genius now?

We know all the answers!

pages 10–11 What is Scratch?

1. A **script** is a set of instructions (program) in Scratch.

2. Objects that perform actions in a project are called **sprites**.

3. In a Scratch program, the action takes place on the **stage**.

4. Starting a program is called **running** it.

5. A collection of sounds or graphics is called a **library**.

pages 16–17 Your First Project

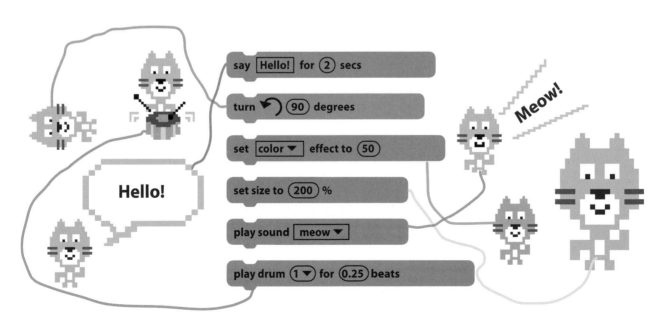

pages 18–19 Move It!

1. What color are the **Motion** blocks? **dark blue**

2. Scratch measures distances in units called **steps**.

2a. How many of these units wide is the stage?

480

2b. How many of these units tall is the stage?

360

3. A mistake in a program is known as a "bug." This script should make the cat move across the stage slowly, but when I click the green flag to run it, nothing happens! What's wrong?

The "when green flag clicked" block is missing.

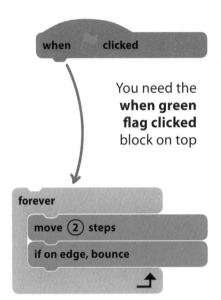

You need the **when green flag clicked** block on top

---

pages 20–21 Which Way?

1. What number should replace the **?** in this block to set the sprite's direction to:

Up = **0**   Left = **–90**

Down = **180**   Right = **90**

2. Test your Scratch script reading powers! What does this script do? Read it carefully and try to act each block out in your mind.

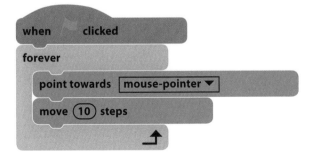

The script makes the cat run toward the cursor on the stage.

pages 22–23 Loops

1. Loops are used to **repeat** groups of blocks.

2. Two types of Scratch loops are **forever** and **repeat**.

3. You can stop a **forever** loop by clicking the **red button**.

4. In which section do you find the pink blocks? **Sound**

5. Which block section has the loops in it? **Control**

6. Bug hunt! This script should draw the four sides of a square, but nothing happens when it's run. Can you spot and suggest a fix for the bug? Programmers call this "debugging."

The repeat loop doesn't say how many repeats to do. Type "4" into its window to fix the bug.

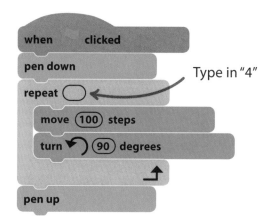

---

pages 24–25 Animation

1. A different picture a sprite can show on the stage is a **costume**.

2. **Animation** is showing pictures with slight differences in order to make a sprite appear to move.

3. Can you rearrange the sprites below to animate a jumping pony? Write the numbers 1 to 5 in the boxes to show the correct order.

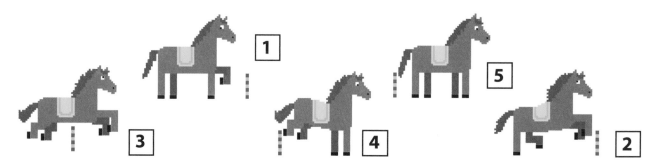

Let's give them the answers!

pages 26–27 Party Time!

1. A background picture on the stage is called a **backdrop**.

2. Circle the block that plays a whole sound before continuing:

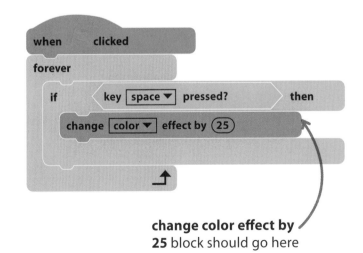

play sound [pop ▼]

play sound [pop ▼] until done

3. True or False?

a. A project can have only one backdrop loaded. **False**

b. Only the sprite that loaded a sound can play it. **True**

c. The stage can have sounds and scripts. **True**

d. Once you've chosen a backdrop for a script, you can't change it. **False**

e. A sprite can use a script to change the stage's backdrop. **True**

---

pages 28–29 if-then

This script should make the sprite change color when you press the space key, but the sprite changes color all the time. Can you spot the "bug"?

The "change color effect by 25" block needs to go inside the "if-then" block.

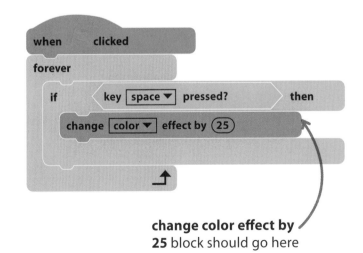

```
when  clicked
forever
    if    key [space ▼] pressed?    then
        change [color ▼] effect by (25)
```

change color effect by 25 block should go here

pages 30–31 Variables

1. A variable has a name and a **value**.

2. Make a Variable button is found in the orange **Data** blocks section.

3. Fill in the speech bubbles for these sets of blocks:

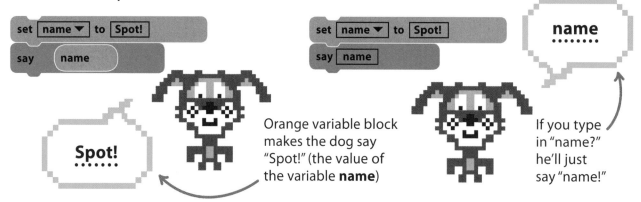

set name ▼ to Spot!
say name

Orange variable block makes the dog say "Spot!" (the value of the variable **name**)

Spot!

set name ▼ to Spot!
say name

If you type in "name?" he'll just say "name!"

name

(Always use the orange variable block to get a variable's value.)

pages 32–33 Math

1. You are the computer! Calculate the values of these blocks.

(3) + (10)   (8) + (11)   (12) − (8)   (22) − (11)   (5) * (6)   (9) / (3)

13   **19**   **4**   **11**   **30**   **3**

2. These blocks use variables. Can you work out the answers?

set a ▼ to 10
set b ▼ to 2

(b) + (6)   (a) − (1)   (a) + (b)   (10) * (b)   (b) − (a)   (b) * (a)   (a) / (5)   (a) / (b)

8   **9**   **12**   **20**   **−8**   **20**   **2**   **5**

3. Write down the values stored in these variables.

set dogs ▼ to 10
set bones each ▼ to 4
set total bones ▼ to (dogs * bones each)

dogs: **10**

bones each: **4**

total bones: **40**

pages 34–35 Input and Events

1. Which blue **Sensing** block makes a sprite ask a question? **ask**

2. Which block holds the reply given to the question? **answer**

3. Something that happens to the computer, like a mouse click or a key press, is called an **event**.

4. What happens if I click a sprite with this script?

The sprite says: "You clicked me!"

5. Can more than one script be running at once? **Yes. (Many scripts can run on many sprites—all at once.)**

---

pages 36–37 if-then-else

1. What shape blocks go into the **condition** window of an **if-then** or **if-then-else** block?

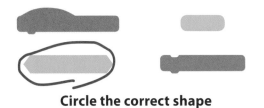

Circle the correct shape

2. Look at the variables below, then circle the green operator blocks that have the value "true."

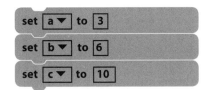

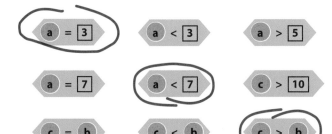

pages 38–39 A Game: Dragon!

1. Why do we leave the check box on the **score** variable checked?

The box is checked so the score is shown on the stage.

2. How could you make the dragon go at half speed at the start?

Change "set speed 10" to "set speed 5."

3. Which block could you add inside the cat's **forever** loop to make it look like it's walking? **The "next costume" block from "Looks."**

4. How many costumes does the dragon have? **2 (You might want to try altering the game script so that the dragon changes costumes when it touches the cat.)**

5. What would happen if you right-clicked the dragon on the sprite list and chose **duplicate**?

You'd find yourself being chased by TWO dragons, and that would make the game very hard!

---

pages 40–47 Sound Party!

1. The **loudness** block reports the volume of sounds detected by the microphone. The volume has a value between **0** and **100**.

2a. To speed up the buttons, increase the number of steps in the **move** block. For example, change it to **loudness + 10**.

2b. To make the buttons' circles smaller, increase the number of degrees in the **turn** block. To make them go the other way, swap the clockwise ↻ **turn** block for the counterclockwise ↺ **turn** block in the **Motion** section.

3. To make the sprite change size only if there is a very loud noise, **80** should go in the window. (Remember: 100 is the loudest volume.)

4.

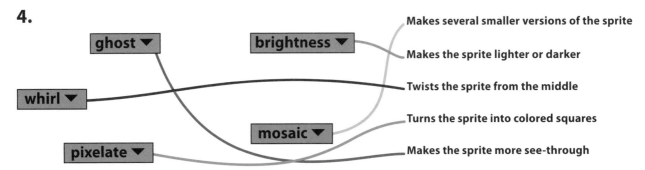

5. Challenge! First, you'll need to change the black backdrop back to white in the paint editor. Then give it a script like this.

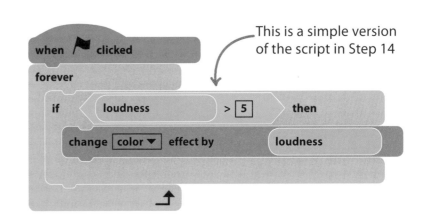

This is a simple version of the script in Step 14

---

pages 48–57 Fishball

1.

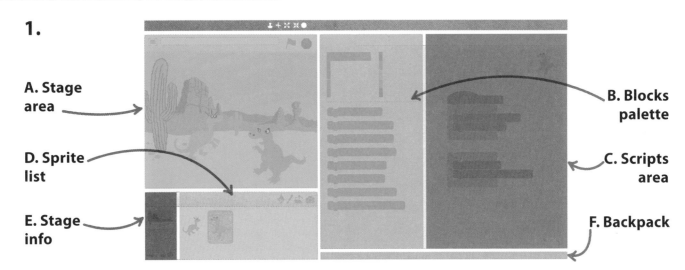

2. A **forever loop** repeats the blocks inside it nonstop.

3. An **if-then** block either skips or runs the blocks inside it.

4. A **variable** is a block that stores data.

5.

Change 1	Change 2
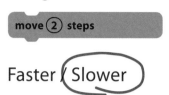	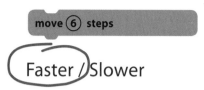

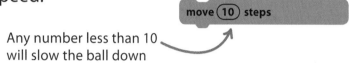

Faster / ~~Slower~~   ~~Faster~~ / Slower

6. To make the ball move slower, change the number in each of its three **move** blocks to less than 10. For example, if you type in 5, the ball will move at half the speed.

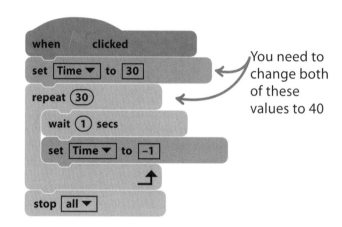

Any number less than 10 will slow the ball down

7. To lengthen the game to 40 seconds, change both values of 30 in the timing script to 40. To make the game shorter, type in values less than 30.

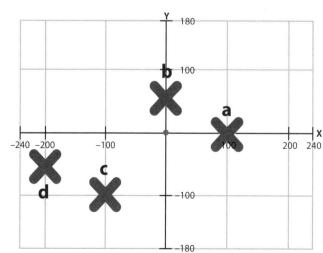

You need to change both of these values to 40

---

pages 58–63 Ghost Hunt

1. Coordinates are always written **(x, y)**.

2. A. (200, 50)   **B.** (−150, 100)   **C.** (200, −150)   **D.** (−50, −100)

3. The x's you drew should be in roughly the same positions as the red x's shown here.

4.

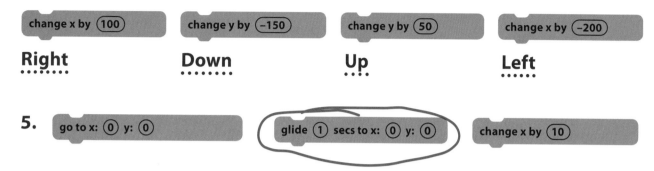

`change x by (100)`   `change y by (−150)`   `change y by (50)`   `change x by (−200)`

Right   **Down**   **Up**   **Left**

5.

`go to x: (0) y: (0)`   `glide (1) secs to x: (0) y: (0)`   `change x by (10)`

6a. To speed up the ghost, reduce its glide time in the **glide** block.

`glide (1) secs to x:` `pick random (−200) to (200)` `y:` `pick random (−150) to (150)`

If you change this to 0.5 seconds,
the ghost will move twice as fast

6b. To slow down the witch, reduce the 10 and −10 steps in her **change x
by** and **change y by** blocks to smaller values, such as 5 and −5.

7. Put the **point in direction 90** block in the witch's right arrow **if-then**
block. The **point in direction −90** block goes in her left arrow **if-then** block.

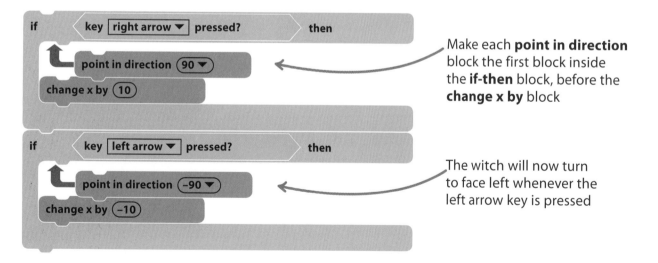

if   key `right arrow ▼` pressed?   then
    point in direction `90 ▼`
change x by (10)

Make each **point in direction**
block the first block inside
the **if-then** block, before the
change x by block

if   key `left arrow ▼` pressed?   then
    point in direction `−90 ▼`
change x by (−10)

The witch will now turn
to face left whenever the
left arrow key is pressed

You'll notice that the poor witch now
spends half her time upside down!
To fix this, select her in the sprite
list, click on the blue **(i)** and change
her rotation style to left–right.

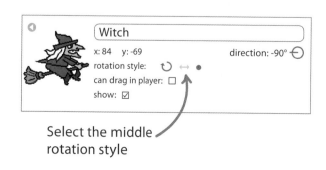

Witch
x: 84   y: -69   direction: -90°
rotation style: ↻ ↔ •
can drag in player: ☐
show: ☑

Select the middle
rotation style

pages 64–69 Rapid Reaction

1. You can resize sprites using the **Grow** and **Shrink** tools above the stage, at the top of the screen.

2. The "scissors" symbol is the delete tool from the bar above the stage.

3. The **timer** block is found in the **Sensing** section of the blocks palette.

4. False: unchecking a variable's checkbox will *hide* the variable, not show it.

5. The coordinates **x:0, y:0** mark the dead center of the stage.

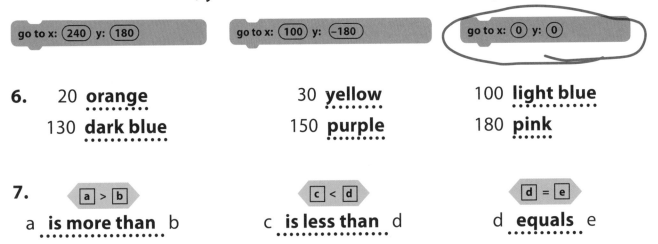

6.   20 **orange**   30 **yellow**   100 **light blue**
      130 **dark blue**   150 **purple**   180 **pink**

7.   a **is more than** b   c **is less than** d   d **equals** e

8. Put the **play sound** blocks inside the players' **if-then** blocks. Don't forget you'll need to load these two sounds from the library if you want to add this code to your game.

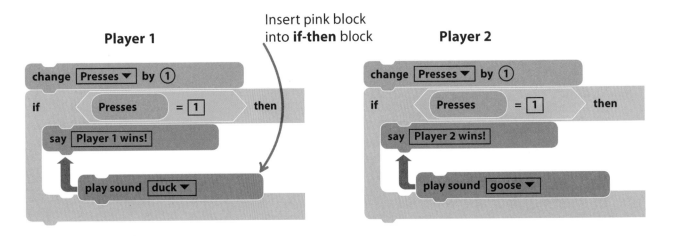

pages 70–75 Keepy-Uppy

1a. The **turn video on**/ **start camera** block switches on the webcam.

2b. We can use the webcam as **input**/ **output** for a Scratch program.

3c. The **turn video off**/ **stop camera** block switches off the video.

2a. Move 30 steps makes the ball move more quickly.

2b. Move 1 steps makes the ball move more slowly.

2c. Move 0 steps stops the ball from moving at all.

3a. False. The score will go up by only 1 point.

3b. True.

3c. False. Any movement can count as hitting the ball—the game can't tell whether it's a hand, foot, or head that makes contact with the ball.

4. The script in Step 13 stops the game when the ball hits the ground. If you remove it, the game will still work and you'll be able to keep hitting the ball even after it has touched the ground.

5. When you change the **when video motion** block to **> 30**, you have to move your body more to hit the ball. This makes the game harder.

6. Challenge! Add these two scripts to the ball. The **timer** block is built into Scratch. It counts the seconds since the program started. We need a new variable, called "**Total Score**," to hold the combined score.

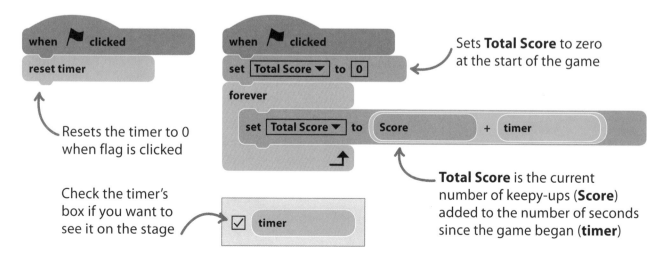

pages 76–81 Monkey Rescue

1. Press the space bar and the cat moves (up)/ down. This means the sprite's **x coordinate** / (**y coordinate**) value will have (**increased**)/ **decreased**.

2a. The value of **Lives** is now 4, since 5 − 1 = 4.

2b. The value of **Lives** is now 10, since 5 + 5 = 10.

2c. The value of **Lives** is now 4, since 1 − 2 = −1, and 5 − 1 = 4.

3. The costumes would change in the order they appear under the **Costumes** tab. This would make the game easier, because you would know when each building was going to scroll across the stage.

4a. (100 , 0)　　　**4b.** (40 , 65)　　　**4c.** (30 , 100)

Remember: The x coordinate is written first and then the y coordinate.

5. Remove the **next costume** block from Step 4. Use the cat's horizontal costume, which glides more easily between the clouds and buildings.

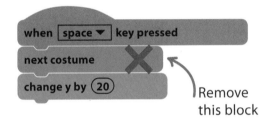

Remove this block

6. Delete the "building-h" costume and change Step 7's **pick random** range to **1 to 9**. Alternatively, make the y value in Step 7's **go to x–y** block a minus number, such as **−40**, so the sprite starts lower down on the stage.

7. Challenge! Make this change to the cloud's **change x by** block. At the start, **Rescued = 0** and the clouds move left in 3-step jumps. Saving a monkey adds an extra step to each jump, making the clouds speed up.

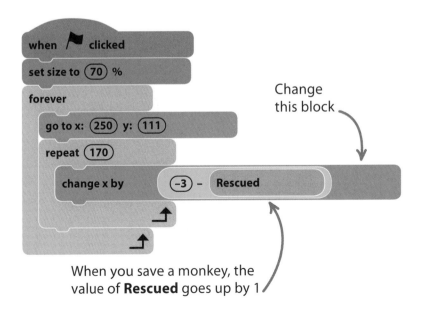

Change this block

When you save a monkey, the value of **Rescued** goes up by 1.

pages 82–89 Memory Master

1a. The (counter)/ **checker** variable is used when the program plays through the sequence of sounds in the list.

1b. The **counter** /(checker) variable is used when the player clicks an instrument.

2. The check box of the **Sound list** is unchecked so the list doesn't show on the stage. The game is about remembering the order of sounds in the list, so it's important that the player doesn't see the contents of the list.

3.

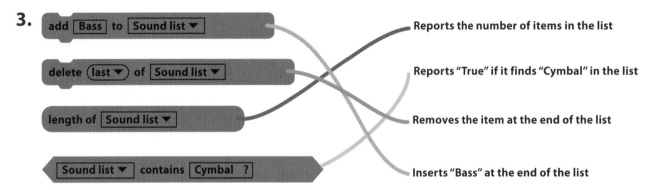

4. In the **delete** block, "**last**" should be "**all**," the **broadcast** message should be "**Add sound**," and the orange block should say "**set Level**."

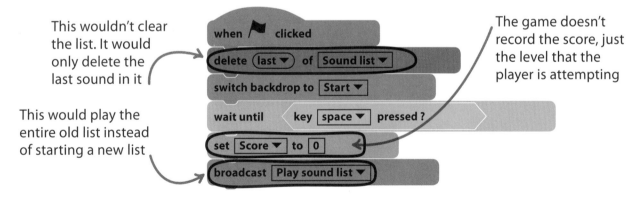

5. Challenge! Copy the Drum-Bass sprite's scripts to the Drum-Tabla. Change the words and messages in the windows to match the new instrument, and choose which of its four sounds you prefer. Add an extra **if-then** block for the Drum-Tabla to each of the stage's two big scripts. Make sure you remember to change the **pick random** block so that its range is now **1 to 5**.

Play the Game!

The aim of the game is to direct your playing piece across the board to the goal without hitting any obstacles in the process.

How to play:

1 Pick an avatar sticker—this will be your playing piece. Stick your avatar onto a square on one side of the board.

2 Place your goal sticker in a square on the opposite side of the board to your avatar.

3 Put the three obstacle stickers around the board, on a square each.

4 Use the instruction blocks to work out a route for your avatar from its starting position to the goal, avoiding the obstacles along the way.

5 Move your avatar around the board, following the instructions you have put together. Do they work? If not, keep changing them until they do.

Make sure you follow the rules!

Now try:

Find a friend to play with, and pick an avatar each. Take turns placing instruction blocks below the board. Who can get to the goal first?

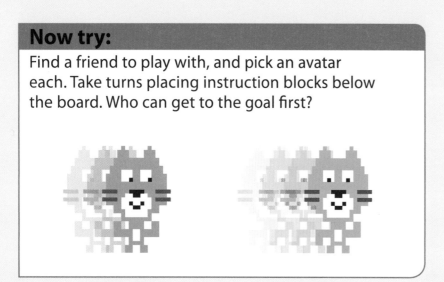

I can't wait to play!

This board is where you will place and direct your pieces.

The avatar is your moving playing piece. There are three colors to choose from.

The dragon, ghost, and shark pieces will block your way—instruct your avatar to avoid them.

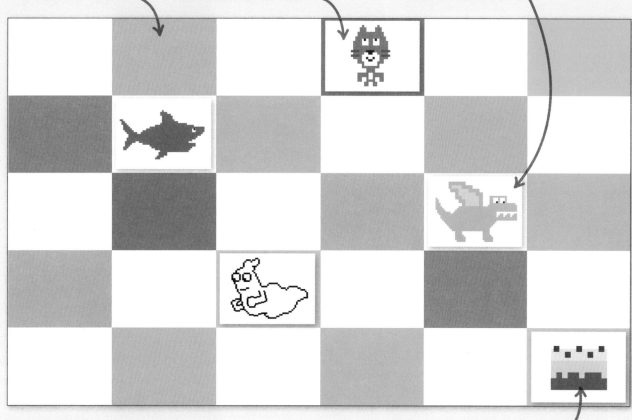

This cake is what you will direct your avatar toward.

Slot your code instructions together in the space under the board.

Put your instructions here!

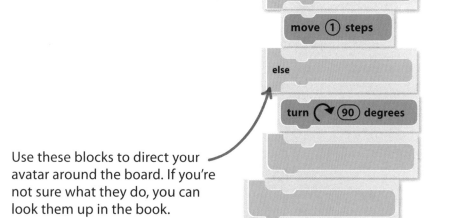

Use these blocks to direct your avatar around the board. If you're not sure what they do, you can look them up in the book.

Happy coding!

Note for parents
The Scratch website is run by Massachusetts Institute of Technology (MIT). It is intended to be safe for children to use. The instructions in this book are for Scratch 2.0, not the older Scratch 1.4. The online version of Scratch works well on Windows, Mac, and Ubuntu computers; the offline version isn't compatible with all Ubuntu versions. At the time of writing, the Raspberry Pi can't run Scratch 2.0. Help your child work logically through any coding difficulties. Check for obvious errors, such as swapping similar blocks in scripts, and that scripts are controlling the correct sprites. Remember: coding should be fun!